A MAN CALLED
JESUS

A MAN CALLED
JESUS

A SERIES OF SHORT PLAYS FROM
THE LIFE OF CHRIST

by

J. B. PHILLIPS

THE MACMILLAN COMPANY

New York   1959

© J. B. Phillips 1959

Library of Congress catalog card number: 59–12520

First Printing

PRINTED IN THE UNITED STATES OF AMERICA

CONTENTS

vi Contents

A MAN CALLED
JESUS

FOREWORD

No one who studies the Gospel records closely can fail to be both stimulated and reverently exasperated by their extreme verbal economy. The lack of detailed information is tantalizing, but it is at the same time stimulating to the imagination. This is, of course, true of all literature, and it is possible for the impact of the skillful short story to be greater than that of the twelve-hundred-page novel. It may therefore be in the providence of God that these art-less unselfconscious pieces of New Testament Greek are really "better" for us than a full-length "biography" of Jesus in the modern sense. The basic facts are given to us, but it is our own God-given imagination which must fill out the picture. We are obliged to think for ourselves, to use heart and mind to make as honest a reconstruction as we can from the material provided. And there is probably no better way of finding out the quality of the Man called Jesus than attempting this very thing.

But we must be on our guard against our own prejudices, and we must never allow sentimentality to creep in. Such reconstruction as we make must not only square with the facts as we know them, but must be completely agreeable with the spirit and character of the Gospels themselves.

We must, as far as is humanly possible, approach the
records without bias. If our minds, for example, are filled
with the ideas of "Jesus the Socialist," "Jesus the Pacifist,"
"Jesus the Rebel," or "Gentle Jesus, meek and mild," the
result of our efforts may be disastrous. To my mind the
late Dorothy Sayers succeeded admirably in authentic
expansion with her play cycle *The Man Born To Be King*.

There is in those plays a faithfulness, a sometimes dis-
concerting faithfulness, to the Gospels themselves. And
intrusion of the writer's own thoughts and feelings is probably kept to the irreducible minimum.

It was with the idea of doing "the same thing for children" that I accepted the B.B.C.'s invitation to write the
following interludes of the life of Jesus for their Schools
Programme. I did not at first see the magnitude of the prob-
lems which were to beset me; perhaps I may set them
down here in order.

1. The age group of the audience would vary from quite
   young children to those about to leave school. Conse-
   quently, although there must be no "writing down,"
   the youngest must not be left in the dark nor must the
   oldest have a childish or inadequate conception of
   the purpose and person of Jesus.
2. I had not realized until I came to write these playlets the
   tyranny of the stop watch. A significant incident must
   be acted intelligibly, and in a sense completely, within
   the limit of about eight minutes. It is necessary to
   establish time, place, character and significance in this
   short period; atmosphere must be quickly created, and
   there is no space to add depth and interest by any
   dialogue which is not strictly necessary. In short, it
   means that not a word must be wasted.

3. These little plays were written for sound radio, and not for television. In the ordinary way I would be found among those who claim that sound radio has very considerable advantages over television in the field of drama. For a receptive and intelligent listener there is almost no limit to the effect of good sound radio. Once the characters are established in the listener's mind they spring to life and are rounded out by his own imagination. He is not distracted, or perhaps indeed annoyed, by visual representations which are very different from his own. And if the play be concerned with a period far removed from the present time, he is not bothered by a difference of clothes, living conditions or, for example, style of architecture. He is set free to *imagine*.

But this is to talk of listening to sound radio in ideal conditions, and I am well aware that to listen in a group during the period of morning worship at school may be a very different thing. The very fact of being "at school" may for some inhibit the powers of imagination, while it is always possible that there are cases of bad reproduction or poor audibility in some of our less well-equipped schools. It seemed to me therefore better to avoid any attempt at subtlety and to delineate the characters and incidents as boldly and clearly as possible.

4. It became necessary in writing these scripts to perform a double feat of imagination: first, to recreate in one's own mind the original Gospel incident and to dramatize it as simply as possible; and secondly, to imagine oneself as the boy or girl in the classroom who can only hear the words that one has written, spoken to them by skillful actors, assisted at times by "noises off." Exactly who is speaking, what people are present and who comes and

goes must be established by sound alone. Crowds may be suggested by the skillful mixing of background noises, but entrances and exits have somehow to be remarked upon—one could not assume that the children would automatically know what the writer had in his mind.

Such considerations appeared at times to be formidable obstacles indeed. But with the good acting which the B.B.C. supplied there seemed to be a real chance for sound radio without visual distraction. The children, at least so one imagined, were not being made to feel by the presence of strange costumes and scenes, that this was a holy legend of long ago and far away. They were meeting something that might well have been contemporary.

5. The interludes had to be written to fit into the framework of a year of school worship. This meant the writing of twenty-six interludes, and it would obviously be impossible for anyone to attempt to write anything approaching a "life of Jesus" within such a small compass. Some careful selection is plainly necessary to give a balanced picture of the character, ministry and purpose of Jesus.

The selected events, simply dramatized, are mostly self-explanatory, but perhaps one or two comments might usefully be made. For example, Interludes 6 and 7 (the healing of the man at Bethesda and of the man born blind) are based on the chronology of the Fourth Gospel. According to John 2: 13, Jesus visited Jerusalem after a brief ministry in Galilee. He returned from Jerusalem to Galilee, according to John 4: 3, but visited the Holy City again soon afterward according to John 5: 1. Of course, the whole business of the chronology of the Gospels is difficult. But it is at least possible that there was an intermittent ministry in Jerusalem and these two interludes were chosen to illustrate this.

The portrayal of the character of Jesus himself, especially on such a small canvas, is very nearly impossible. But some attempt was made to show that he possessed strength as well as tenderness, a steellike toughness as well as sympathy, and the most extraordinary courage as well as perfect obedience.

It was also felt important that the children should see that the Pharisees were not necessarily all villains. It is true that those whose hypocrisy and pride had been exposed by Jesus were successful in destroying him; but it is surely possible that Nicodemus was not the only one to have serious doubts. Some attempt has therefore been made to suggest that not all the religious leaders were necessarily determined to have Jesus executed.

The character of Judas will always remain an enigma. The most a dramatist can do is to suggest some reason for the sudden and terrible betrayal. To my mind Judas was a man who greatly admired power and strength, and who could indeed sympathize with many of the ideas of the Master, provided they were backed by the force of his personality. But when he found Jesus taking what appeared to be the line of weakness, when Jesus appeared perfectly willing to surrender to the forces of evil, then Judas was completely disillusioned. He felt himself betrayed and his devotion turned into violent contempt.

For the most part the scripts are published "as broadcast," and I am grateful to the producers, Robert Walton and George Dixon, for the skill they displayed in making small alterations here and there. From their long experience, they know that some words do not "sound" well, or do not "register" properly when the audience can hear but not see the facial expression. I was privileged to attend two rehearsals of these interludes, and I must record my profound admiration for the enormous care taken in presenting them. Nothing was too much trouble for either producers or actors in their effort to make the playlets live. And there was a most moving sincerity and reverence in the studio when rehearsal was over and the play was "on."

It was suggested to me that many people might like to have these broadcasts in permanent form, not least the teachers in our schools. I hope that being able to refer to the actual broadcast material may help them in the questions and discussion which sometimes follow a religious broadcast. It is also hoped that this simple imaginative approach to familiar stories may help others, not forgetting the large number of "shut-ins" and bedridden, to picture for themselves more readily the kind of circumstances which may clothe the bare bones of the Gospel narrative.

Quite a number of schools, churches, clubs and other groups attempt at Christmas, Passiontide or at other times of the Church's year, to present in simple drama some events in the life of the Man called Jesus. It is hoped that these plays, which are free from archaisms and special "religious" language, may serve as a guide for such production, which usually needs a minimum of costume and scenery.

I should like to express here my gratitude to the British Broadcasting Corporation for their help in producing these interludes in book form.

SWANAGE, DORSET   J. B. PHILLIPS
      1959

SOME NOTES ON CHARACTERIZATION

ANDREW. I see him in about the same stage of compre-
hension as Peter. But he is somewhat more thoughtful
and more cautious.

CAIAPHAS. A cold, calculating man who knows himself
to be the intellectual superior of his fellows. It does
not enter his head for a single second that there could
be any doubt as to what should happen to Jesus, the
field preacher.

JAMES and JOHN. I cannot see much difference in character between these two brothers from the Gospel
records. I see them as passionately loyal followers of
Jesus, with possibly a tendency to bluster which
earned them from Jesus the nickname "the Thun-
derers."

JESUS (*as a boy*). He must not have a holy voice, neither
must he sound pert. At this stage he is a normal intelligent boy with a questioning mind and, I imagine, it is
only just beginning to dawn upon him that he is
uniquely the Son of God.

(*In "The Temptation" story only*) He is a man exhausted physically but not spiritually. His prayers

must not be plaintive but confident, despite extreme weariness.

To my mind there should often be a smile in his voice since he is genuinely fond of the disciples and appreciates their loyalty. At the same time he is the Master speaking to learners, and on occasion his voice hardens into seriousness but never into solemn pulpit tones. We need great flexibility of voice for Jesus must be able to speak with humor, with gentleness, with authority and, as in the Caesarea-Philippi episode, with a prophetic seriousness. But generally in the early scenes Jesus expresses hope and confidence. Humanly speaking, he has not yet fully realized the inevitable collapse of his plans.

Eventually, when he sees what must happen to him there is a sense of unflinching dedication which alarms the disciples. After the Resurrection there must be a hint of higher authority. He is the triumphant King to whom "all power is given."

JOHN THE BAPTIST (*as a boy*).   He is as yet still boyish, and should speak quite naturally.

(*At the baptisms*) He must sound like an O.T. prophet. He is so sure of the Message of God that he fears no man, however exalted. Therefore his sudden contact with Jesus which abashes and overawes him is the more dramatically telling.

JOSEPH.   Tradition, though not the New Testament, sees him as a man much older than Mary. I do not see why he should be an old man, although he was probably older than Mary. He is strongly protective and, I think, despite his puzzlement, determined to do his duty as "father" to the extraordinary child.

JUDAS ISCARIOT.   I see him as a "tough" character, probably tougher than any of the others. He is filled with
admiration for Jesus' self-discipline and spiritual drive.
He is strongly attracted by the Person of Jesus and can
probably see better than the others the possibilities of
the "Kingdom." But he is going to be disillusioned because of the apparent weakness of Jesus' methods.
In the early days, however, his own tough idealism is
enormously impressed by Jesus.

MARY MAGDALENE.   It is important to remember that before becoming a disciple of Jesus she had been en-
slaved by her emotions and passions—("out of whom
he had cast seven devils"). She had given her complete heart loyalty to Jesus. Possibly to a woman of
her temperament the loss of Jesus' body following his
terrible death makes her almost hysterically inconsol-
able. She has not even the body of her Lord to weep
over.

MARY THE VIRGIN.   I think she should not be terribly "lady-
like"! This is not the Queen of Heaven speaking, but a
thoroughly good and supremely natural woman. She
is at all times full of faith, but she is sometimes strained
by the almost overwhelming responsibility she has
to bear.

MATTHEW.   I see him as a man who has hitherto been
rather despised and underrated by his fellow men. He
is tremendously thrilled that Jesus has seen through
the front he presents to the world and called to the
real man within. At the same time, I think in the early
stages he is a little nervous and unsure of himself.

NICODEMUS.   Both he and the sympathetic scribe are in-
troduced in the Crucifixion scene to show that prob-

ably not all the religious leaders were blind to the truth of the teaching of Jesus. Some indeed might be beginning secretly to believe his claims.

PETER. I do not necessarily see him as "the big fisherman"! But he is sensitive, enthusiastic and impetuous. He is Jesus' loyal supporter, but he has very little insight as to what Jesus is in fact setting out to do. Even after the Resurrection he is not very quick to understand.

PONTIUS PILATE. He is a man torn between the desire to assert his authority over these troublesome Jews and thus to remain a friend of Caesar, and the desire to be fair to this extraordinary Man with whom he is confronted. His nervousness and agitation should show through his air of authority.

SATAN. A very flexible voice is required here, which can threaten, cajole, despise, or flatter with a horrifying dexterity. I should like there to be an undertone of both power and hatred, but this naturally must not be overdone or it will produce something of a stage demon king. It would be fine if the children could feel that evil is real and ingenious in its methods, and yet can be defeated.

1

THE BOYHOOD OF JESUS

Now the parents of Jesus went to Jerusalem every year at
the feast of the Passover. And when he was twelve years
old, they went up to Jerusalem after the custom of the
feast. And when the feast was ended, as they returned, the
child Jesus stayed behind in Jerusalem; and Joseph and
his mother did not know it. But they, supposing him to
have been in the company, went a day's journey.

(*Scene: A day's journey from Jerusalem. The caravansery
has halted and there could be noises of unharnessing,
stamping of hoofs, camel bells, murmur of voices, etc.*)

JOSEPH.   Well, Mary, this has been a wonderful week. But
(*with quick concern*) it's been tiring for you, my dear,
meeting so many people. All our party are stopping
here for the night. I'll get a fire going, for it gets a bit
chilly in the evenings. Then you can be comfortable
and rest.

MARY.   Thank you, Joseph, I am a little tired, but it was
well worth it.

JOSEPH (*proudly*).   Yes, indeed! When I see all our people gathered together at Passover time, I feel more

proud than ever to know that I belong to the royal line of King David.

MARY (*softly*). Yes, and to think that we've seen Jesus and his cousin John become sons of the Law! Why it makes them seem almost grown up.

JOSEPH (*good-humoredly.*). Well, not quite that, Mary, but they're certainly no longer mere children. (*Pause. Adds reminiscently*) Strange how the years have passed. It doesn't seem so very long to me since . . . Bethlehem, and taking the child up to the Temple, and then having to fly for our lives into Egypt. It's been a strange life for you, my dear, looking back on it.

MARY (*gently*). I'm not complaining about that, Joseph. I've never forgotten all that was told me about him when he was a baby.

JOSEPH (*tenderly*). Well, you have no need to worry, Mary, whatever happens. There's not another woman whose life belongs so completely to the Lord as yours does! But this Jesus of ours certainly isn't the only unusual child—did you notice his cousin John?

MARY (*thoughtfully*). Yes. His dark eyes were watching everybody, yet he hardly spoke a word.

JOSEPH. I believe his mother is a bit worried.

MARY. She tells me he seems to be happiest when he's by himself. He'll go off and spend all day, and sometimes half the night on the hillside. When he comes back and she asks him what he's been doing, he says, "Oh, I've been thinking."

JOSEPH. Yes, he's a thoughtful lad all right. But what a difference between those two! Our Jesus took in all that was going on. He watched the priests at the Sacrifice, he joined in the singing and the prayers, and at the feast itself, he was the one to ask me what it all meant. Yet all the week he seemed to want to talk to people and ask them questions, while John seemed, well, withdrawn.

MARY. Yes, but, praise the Lord, they're good friends. I wonder where they are.

JOSEPH. Oh, I expect they're somewhere in our crowd. Ah, there's John, over there with his parents, but I don't see Jesus. I'll call him. (*Calls*) John! John!

JOHN. Yes, Uncle Joseph?

JOSEPH. Have you seen Jesus anywhere?

JOHN. No, I thought he was with you.

JOSEPH. Come over here a minute.

JOHN. We have been together most of the week, but now and again I want to be on my own. Anyway, I expect he's in our party somewhere. I shouldn't worry, uncle.

JOSEPH. We're not worrying, John. But just to set his mother's mind at rest, pass the word along to see if anyone's seen him, will you?

JOHN. Certainly, uncle. (*Goes off, shouting*) Jesus, you're wanted! Anyone seen Jesus, son of Joseph and Mary? Anyone seen Jesus of Nazareth? Jesus, your parents want you! (*Voice growing gradually more distant*).

And they sought him among their kinsfolk and acquaintance. And when they found him not, they turned back again to Jerusalem, seeking him.

(*Scene: A street in Jerusalem near the Temple. Subdued noises of crowd.*)

MARY (*a little breathlessly*). Joseph, I can't help feeling anxious now.

JOSEPH. Yes, Mary, I know.

MARY. This is the third day we've spent looking for Jesus, and it seems so hopeless in all this crowd. It isn't like him to cause us all this distress. I feel sure something must have happened to him.

JOSEPH. Now, Mary, we must not worry. He's a special child and we can be sure he's in God's special care. They say a million of us Jews have been to the Passover this year, and a boy could get lost in such a crowd. But we're a kindly race.

MARY. Yes, but where is he?

JOSEPH. Someone will have given him food and shelter, I'm sure; you know how many friends he has.

MARY (*uncomforted*). I suppose it's no good asking one of those Roman soldiers at the corner?

JOSEPH (*in a hard voice*). No, I don't think so. What's one little Jewish boy to them? In their eyes they all look alike anyway.

MARY. Well, then I think we ought to try the Temple. Some of the wise teachers there will surely be able to advise us.

And it came to pass, that after three days they found him in the Temple, sitting in the midst of the teachers, both hearing them, and asking them questions.

(*Scene: Inside one of the Temple courts: Rabbis holding informal conversation with small crowd present.*)

1ST RABBI. And so, my son, the Lord has chosen us to be his own peculiar people.

ONLOOKER. Yes, that's right.

JESUS. But what of these others, these Romans who occupy our country? Has our God no love or purpose for them?

1ST RABBI. That's a strange question from a Jewish lad.

ONLOOKER. No, let him ask. I've often wondered about that myself.

2ND RABBI (*contemptuously*). The Romans are but dogs of Gentiles, men without the Law, men without God! When the Messiah comes he will throw off the yoke and drive the heathen back whence they came.

JESUS (*puzzled*). But does not the prophet Isaiah foretell that the Messiah will bring light to the Gentiles?

ONLOOKER. Yes, that's in the Prophets all right.

2ND RABBI. Not until they're beaten to their knees, my son. Not until the strong right arm of the Lord has been revealed through His chosen Servant!

JESUS (*a little shocked*). I do not understand. Do you tell me that the Lord God will force the Gentiles by fear and terror to love Him?

MARY (*breaking in*). Jesus, Jesus! We've found you at last!

JOSEPH (*apologetically*). Excuse us, sirs; we're his parents. His mother has been very anxious.

1ST RABBI. The boy's mother? By all means let her speak.

MARY (*ignoring all but Jesus*). How could you do a thing like this to us, my son? Your father and I have been looking for you everywhere for three days. Can't you see how you've worried us?

JESUS. Mother, I'm sorry that you have been worried. But why did you look for me *everywhere*. Here in my Father's House is where I *had* to be.

MARY (*desperately, not understanding*). Oh, Jesus, my son!

JOSEPH (*puzzled and stern*). I'm not sure, my son, that

that makes as good sense to us as it evidently does to you. But come now, get your things, and come back to Nazareth with us. For the next few years you must do what we tell you, and be a good son in your own home.

JESUS.   Yes, I will come. The Law says that I must honor my father and my mother, and that I will gladly do.

2

THE BAPTISM OF JESUS

Now in the fifteenth year of Tiberius Caesar, Pontius Pilate being governor of Judaea, the word of God came unto John, the son of Zacharias. And he came into all the region round about Jordan preaching the baptism of repentance for the forgiveness of sins.

(*Scene: The open countryside on the banks of the Jordan.*)

FATHER. Don't be frightened, Isaac, my son, just keep close to my side.

LITTLE BOY (Isaac). Father, is that the man we've come all this way to see? I'm not sure I like him. He looks so fierce and his voice makes me feel frightened. What are all these crowds here for?

JOHN (*speaking in ringing tones against background murmur of voices*). Men of Israel, I come from the naked desert where no man spoke to me, but I come with the word of the Lord. I come as His messenger, and His message is this:

Repent, every one of you! Forsake your sins and your shame, your greed and your pride! Rich and poor, high and low, every one of you needs to repent of his sins. I will baptize you here in the waters of Jordan, as a sign that your sins are washed away! Repent, I say to you, repent . . .

(*Fade out* JOHN's *voice.*)

FATHER. Yes, this is the man we came to hear. His name is John, and he's a stern man, like one of the old prophets.

ISAAC. What are all these crowds here for?

FATHER. My son, John is calling men to be sorry for their sins, and then he's washing them in the river as a sign that they're made clean in the eyes of God.

ISAAC (*rather excitedly*). You mean he's really like one of the prophets we hear read to us in the Synagogue?

FATHER. Yes, just like that, Isaac.

(*Fade in* JOHN's *voice.*)

JOHN. . . . and hundreds of you already have publicly owned your sins and been baptized.

FATHER. Listen to what he's saying now.

JOHN. . . . Men and women of Israel, I am that voice which the prophet foretold, that voice crying in the wilderness, "Make ready the way of the Lord, make his paths straight!" I am the herald of the King and I tell you that the Kingdom of God is coming, not a hundred years hence, but now, today, it is here at your doors! Every one of you must be ready for that Kingdom. I beg you, nay, I command you to repent, repent . . .

(*Fade out* JOHN's *voice.*)

FATHER (*in an eager whisper*). Look, son, how his words are striking home—here come some of the priests, and he's evidently hit them hard.

ISAAC (*incredulously*). What, father, are priests wicked and sinful too?

FATHER. Hush, my son, and listen.

(Fade in JOHN's *voice).*

JOHN. The Lord God calls all men to repent, for all have
sinned. And you priests, you serpent's brood, who
warned you to come out from your holes and corners,
and escape from the wrath to come? I know your
hypocrisy, I know your pride, your love of power,
and all your secret sins. If you come in repentance, I
welcome you to the waters of Jordan. But if you come
in your pride, I refuse you utterly! And do not go on
thinking that you are safe and secure because you are
children of Abraham, and that therefore you must be
favored by God. Children of Abraham! Why the Lord
God Almighty could turn these stones at my feet into
children of Abraham if He so desired. Show by your
lives that you have truly repented! Come then, all
those who truly and earnestly repent of their sins. . . .

(Fade out JOHN's *voice.)*

FATHER *(heaving a sigh).*   Well, I never thought I'd live to
see such a day.

ISAAC. What is it, father?

FATHER *(in awed tones).*   Isaac, my son, some of the
priests themselves are going down and being baptized.
And, yes, there are some Roman soldiers, too! The
power of God is certainly with this man John. Who
would ever have though it possible that priests and
Roman soldiers could show their repentance openly
like that?

JOHN *(rather more gently).*   Come and be cleansed in the
Name of the Lord. May the Lord bless you and keep
you in the ways of righteousness.

PHARISEE (*with authority*). I am a Pharisee, I must know the truth. Are you the Messiah then, you who speak in the Name of the Lord and wash men's sins away?

JOHN. No, I am not! I have told you, I am only the voice that cries "Repent." I come only to prepare the way of the One Who shall come. Indeed I am not worthy to carry His shoes! I am nothing, but He is everything. The One Who is coming, He is infinitely stronger than I. He will baptize you with the Holy Spirit and with fire! He comes prepared to judge His people, to separate the wheat from the chaff. The chaff He will burn with a fire that no man can put out! The One Who comes after me. . . .

JESUS. John.

(*During the last two sentences of* JOHN's *oration the crowd noises are stilled, for* JESUS *is making His way toward* JOHN. *There is a moment's utter silence.*)

JOHN (*awestruck*). You, who are you?

JESUS (*gently*). I am Jesus of Nazareth.

JOHN. Jesus!

JESUS. Do you not know me, cousin John?

JOHN (*awed*). Jesus—why have you come here?

JESUS (*simply*). I have come as other men have come, John, to be baptized by you.

JOHN (*utterly shaken*). Never! Never would I do such a thing! Jesus, it is I who should be coming to you, in repentance for all my sins. It is you who should baptize me. I am not worthy to baptize you! I—

JESUS (*gently but firmly*). John, this is the Will of our Father. Let us go down into the waters of the river together. For I am come as a Man amongst men, and I must meet all the Law's demands.

JOHN (*humbly*).　Then let it be as you say, Lord.

(*A pause, followed by a sudden crack of thunder and a long, rumbling peal.*)

JOHN (*in an awed whisper*).　That voice spoke to you! You *are* the Promised One! You *are* the beloved Son!

JESUS (*half to himself*).　Father, give me strength always to do Thy will.

ISAAC (*hoarse with excitement*).　Did you hear that Voice, father? Was it God speaking to him? Is he someone very special?

FATHER.　Yes, my son, very, very special. I believe with all my heart that we have seen with our own eyes the Messiah, God's Christ.

❧ 3 ❧

THE TEMPTATION OF JESUS

Then was Jesus led by the Spirit into the wilderness, being tempted by the devil for forty days. And in those days he ate nothing; and after they were ended, he was hungry.

(Noise of wind blowing through dry bushes. Sound of distant jackals howling, and roar of mountain lion.)

SATAN *(insinuatingly)*. Listen, Jesus, do you remember how the Scripture says the young lions roar after their prey and seek their meat from God? But sometimes the young lions do lack and suffer hunger. . . . And do you remember how that verse of the psalm goes on? They that seek the Lord shall not want any good thing. *(With sudden emphasis)* Now what about food? *Food*, eh, isn't that a "good thing"? And haven't you been "seeking the Lord" for forty days and forty nights?

JESUS *(praying)*. O Lord, my God, in Thee have I put my trust, save and deliver me in my weakness.

SATAN *(shortly)*. Come now, praying won't fill your stomach, you know. It's food you want.

JESUS *(praying)*. Father, uphold me, according to Thy

word, that I may live and let me not be ashamed of my hope.

SATAN (*losing patience*).   Oh, that's enough of quoting Scripture. A man needs food—you're tired and faint and dizzy, so that you can't even trust your own eyesight. Look at these round flat things. Are they newly baked loaves, smelling good and sweet, straight from the oven?

JESUS (*stolidly*).   They are stones.

SATAN (*persuasively*).   But how easily, how easily, with a snap of the fingers as you might say, could you turn them into bread. (*Commandingly*) If you really are the Son of God, turn these stones into bread! (*Coaxingly*) It isn't only for yourself, you know. Think what a following you would have if you could satisfy the hungry millions of the world! Give them food and they'll follow you anywhere.

JESUS (*wearily, but steadily*).   It is written, Man shall not live by bread alone, but by every word that proceedeth out of the mouth of God.

Then the devil taketh him up into the Holy City and setteth him on a pinnacle of the Temple.

(*Sound of wind blowing to suggest height.*)

SATAN.   It feels strange, doesn't it, up here on the very highest point of the Temple, with the wind whipping your cloak out like a flag? It's cold, too, after the heat of the desert. Come now, you're trembling. Why didn't you eat some food when I told you to? Six weeks without a bite of food are bound to make a man faint and weak and giddy.

JESUS (*praying*).   Father, hold Thou me up and I shall be safe.

SATAN.   Open your eyes now and look at all those people in the courtyard below. They're your people, the people you've come to save, remember? And how are you going to start, eh? How are you going to make your entrance? I'll tell you: just let go! You won't hurt yourself—you'll go floating down there as if you were on wings, with thousands of pairs of eyes watching you in amazement. They'll all cry out, "the Messiah has arrived, by a miracle!" There's nothing people like more than a good miracle. You can be sure of that.

JESUS(*praying*).   Father, save me from the dangers and snares of the enemy.

SATAN (*contemptuously*).   If you really are the Son of God, there's no danger at all. Have you forgotten the Scriptures? I never forget them. Don't you remember the promise which says, "He shall give his angels charge concerning thee, and in their hands they shall bear thee up, lest at any time thou dash thy foot against a stone"?

JESUS (*firmly*).   But the Scripture also says, "Thou shalt not put the Lord thy God to the test."

Again the devil taketh him up into an exceedingly high mountain and showeth him all the kingdoms of the world and the glory of them.

(*The wind now rises to a shriek as though whirling* JESUS *and* SATAN *away to the top of the high mountain. Then the wind dies down.*)

SATAN.   And now we're higher still, looking down on the world, as the angels do—or the devils, for that matter.

Can you see, Jesus, can you see all the pomp and glory, the might and majesty of all the world's kingdoms? Who do you think they belong to? They're mine, *mine!*

JESUS.   But I see also many ordinary men and women at their work. I see children at play and happy homes. I see men and women doing works of mercy, healing the sick and caring for the aged. . . .

SATAN (*interrupting impatiently*).   Yes, yes, but they're not the important ones. Who do you suppose has the power, the riches and the glory? Those things are all in the hands of my men. Now, just a little gesture from you, just a little acknowledgment that I'm the real master of the powers of this world, and I'll step aside and give it all to you. (*Scornfully*) You Son of God!

JESUS (*with desperate strength*).   Away with you, Satan. Think what you will, but at the last you will see that all power belongs to God. The Scripture says, "Thou shalt worship the Lord thy God, and him only shalt thou serve"!

Then the devil leaveth him, and, behold, angels came and ministered unto him.

4

THE CALLING OF THE DISCIPLES

After John was put in prison, Jesus came into Galilee, preaching the gospel of the kingdom of God, and saying, The time is fulfilled, and the kingdom of God is at hand: repent ye, and believe the gospel.

(Noise of the lapping of water, the stirring of feet through the shallows, and the occasional swish of the hand net as it is raised. JAMES and JOHN are quite near by, sitting in the shade of their boat.)

ANDREW. You know, Peter, this working the net in the shallows reminds me of when we were children.

PETER. H'm. When we were children, Andrew, we were always hopeful—always expecting to catch some big one that the grown-ups had missed.

ANDREW (*yawning*). Well, there's no harm in being hopeful, though last night's work with James and John was pretty depressing. Hours and hours out there on the lake and not a fish to show for it. By the way, what are those two doing, I wonder?

PETER. I don't know, I'll give them a shout. (*He calls*) Ahoy there, James and John! Are you awake?

26

JOHN (*from a short distance away, a shade indignantly*). Of course, we're awake, and working.

JAMES. You don't mind if we mend the nets on the shady side of the boat where you can't see us?

PETER (*good-temperedly*). Certainly not, as long as you don't drop off to sleep! I've a feeling there's going to be a lot of work for us all to do before long.

JOHN. Well, I hope you're right. See you later!

PETER. All right, get on with the good work! (*No longer hailing*) And we'd better get on with ours, Andrew.

ANDREW. Got him! A little one, but he'll do all right for dinner.

PETER. And here's another one. Andrew, my lad, we're doing better in the shallows. I wonder why we lose our beauty sleep going out all night with the big net. (*Snorts scornfully.*)

ANDREW (*thoughtfully*). I sometimes wonder why we waste our lives being fishermen at all.

PETER (*teasingly*). Andrew, you amaze me! To hear such a thing from you—a quiet, even tempered, steady-going fisherman! What on earth do you mean?

ANDREW. Ah! (*Straightening his back*) Let's straighten up for a moment. Well, the truth is that ever since I heard John the Baptist preaching out there in the desert, I've had a strong feeling that there are more important things in life than just catching fish.

PETER (*seriously*). I never guessed he disturbed you, Andrew. I admit he touched me all right. He spoke with the real power of God, that man did. And when I saw hundreds of people admitting their sins and being baptized, why I thought it was the Messiah himself come at last!

ANDREW. But John the Baptist particularly denied that,

Peter. He said there was One coming after him, far greater than himself. He would be the One to found the Kingdom of God, whatever that means.

PETER.   Yes, yes, I know, but I heard last night that a man arrived from Nazareth, an ordinary workingman as far as anyone could see—carpenter, I believe—and John as good as said that *he* was the Messiah.

ANDREW.   Yes, I heard that too. He's certainly got the right name. He's called Jesus—you know, same as Joshua, means Deliverer, Rescuer, Saviour, or something.

PETER.   I did hear that this Man Jesus is carrying on John's work here in Galilee, now that John's gone.

ANDREW (*with unexpected bitterness*).   That was a foul business. What faith can you have in life when a drunken lout like Herod can imprison a saint like John the Baptist? I saw that man, I heard him and I believed him, and now he's gone, shut up in the filthy prison. As for this Jesus, we've only got rumor to go on.

PETER.   Ah, I think it's a bit more than rumor, Andrew. The fellows I was talking to last night said they'd actually seen and heard Jesus, here in Galilee.

ANDREW.   Well, what was he saying—same as John?

PETER (*thoughtfully*).   Well, not quite. True, he's calling people to repent of their sins, just as John did. But he's also calling them to accept this new Kingdom of God. He speaks as though it's already here and now. I admit I don't understand . . .

ANDREW (*interrupting*).   Who's this? Someone's walking straight toward us.

PETER (*indifferently*).   Stranger to me. Anyway, let him do the talking.

JESUS. Greetings to you, Peter and Andrew! I am Jesus of Nazareth, and I have a message for you.

PETER (*slowly*). Jesus of Nazareth! What message can you have for us . . . sir?

JESUS. Here is my message. Follow me, and I will make you fishers of men.

PETER. Fishers of men?

JESUS. Yes, follow me, and help me catch men for the Kingdom of God, the Kingdom of my Father. I can promise you plenty of work, hardships, disappointments, dangers, yes, all these and the joy and glory of working for the eternal Kingdom of God. But if you come there must be no looking back. Do you understand?

PETER and ANDREW (*together*). Yes.

JESUS. Then, will you come?

PETER. Yes, I'll come, sir.

ANDREW. You can count on me, sir.

JESUS. Now what about your partners, James and John? I have to call them too. Let's go over to the boat and meet them. I need men like that. (*He calls as He approaches*) James and John?

JAMES and JOHN. Yes. You're looking for us?

JESUS. I am Jesus of Nazareth, and I have a message for you.

JOHN (*a little guardedly*). I'm John, and this is my brother James. What message have you for us?

JESUS. A direct and personal one. I want you to leave your fishing, to leave your father. Instead of catching fish, I want to teach you to catch men for the Kingdom of God.

PETER (*interrupting*). We've already . . .

JESUS. Hush, Peter! James and John, you have heard
already from John the Baptist something of the Kingdom of God. Are you willing to leave everything and
help me build that Kingdom? Are you willing to come
at once?

JOHN. I am perfectly willing; I will come at once.

JAMES. I feel the same way as my brother, sir, and I will
come too.

∽ 5 ∽

THE HEALING OF
THE PARALYZED MAN

Jesus entered into Capernaum after some days; and a rumor spread that he was in the house. And straightway many were gathered together, insomuch that there was no room to receive them, not so much as about the door; and he preached the word unto them.

(*Scene: Outside the house where* JESUS *is teaching. Murmur of crowd in background.*)

FRUIT PORTER.   Je—hoshaphat, what a crowd! Make way there, *please,* I've got to get this fruit to market and I'm late already. Mind your backs! (*Grumbling*) What is all this fuss, anyway? Haven't you got any work to do, because I have? Make way, make way— *please!*

WOMAN IN CROWD.   All right, all right, no need to push like that. Don't you know the Master's inside this house, and we all want to catch a glimpse of him as he comes out since none of us could get inside.

FRUIT PORTER.   Master? What master? The master I work

for's going to be pretty angry if I don't get my work done.

WOMAN. Why, *the* Master, Jesus of Nazareth! Weren't you here a few days ago?

A BYSTANDER. That was something I wouldn't have missed for the world. I've never heard a man speak like that.

WOMAN. Yes, and the way he healed people! I wasn't actually there, but he completely cured poor old Benjamin the leper. Hark at me—"poor old Benjamin"! But he's healed now, passed fit by the priests, and back at work.

FRUIT PORTER (*not very impressed*). Well, I don't live here in Capernaum and your excitements are none of my business. I've got to get this fruit to market, crowds or no crowds. So make way there, please, make way for a poor workingman who can't take time off for miracles.

(*Some good-tempered laughter.*)

WOMAN (*good-naturedly*). Well, pity he couldn't stay. But look, what's coming now?

(*Approaching voices of* FOUR *young men carrying paralytic on stretcher.*)

1ST MAN. Make way there, please, for a sick man.

2ND MAN. We've got to get him to Jesus.

3RD MAN. Come on, please stand back and let us through.

BYSTANDER. What do you young fellows want barging in?

4TH MAN. Have a heart—how would you like to be paralyzed?

WOMAN. Oh, it's you lads, is it? Now just you stop shoving for a minute and be reasonable. How d'you think you're going to get that stretcher inside the house?

Why we've been waiting here for hours and we can't get in!

BYSTANDER.   Not even sideways! (*Good-tempered laughter.*)

1ST MAN.   But we *must*. If other people would only be reasonable and make way. . . .

2ND MAN.   We must get him to Jesus! Can't you see he's helpless? We've got to get him healed. He's our friend —we five have been together since we were children, and we know the Master can heal him.

WOMAN (*firmly*).   It's no use, my sons, people are packed together like figs in a box. Some things are impossible, and getting that stretcher into this house is one of them.

3RD MAN.   All right, then, but we'll find some way! (*Lowering his voice*) What about going round the back, and up the outside stairs?

4TH MAN (*quietly*).   Good idea!

(*Fade out voices and hubbub of crowd.*)

(*Scene: Now inside house,* JESUS *has stopped speaking for a moment, there is murmur of conversation.*)

1ST SCRIBE (*petulantly*).   I do wish those people outside wouldn't make such a noise. At times I can hardly hear what this Jesus is saying.

(*Cracking and scraping noises overhead as tiles are removed.*)

2ND SCRIBE.   Yes, these interruptions are intolerable. Whatever we may decide about this man, what he says is obviously important. You wouldn't find the Pharisees

or even any of us Scribes coming down here unless he
had to be taken seriously.

(*The noise overhead grows louder.*)

1ST SCRIBE (*in exasperation*).   I really do believe they're
    going to try and come in through the roof now! It's
    insufferable!

JESUS.   The Son of Man comes not to call the righteous,
    but sinners—to repentance. It is not the healthy who
    need the doctor, but the sick. And there are many sick,
    sick in soul and sick in mind, as well as sick in body.

(*There is a final rending sound and* JESUS *looks up.*)

JESUS.   But now I see we have visitors from the skies (*in
    mock severity*). And what is the meaning of this?

1ST MAN.   Sir, Master, we *had* to bring our friend to you—
    he's paralyzed.

2ND MAN.   And we knew you could cure him. Here, steady
    with that rope—lower him gently.

3RD MAN.   Steady it is, he's nearly down now.

4TH MAN (*pleadingly*).   Master, we couldn't think of any
    other way. We promise we'll put the roof back after
    you've healed our friend.

JESUS.   So you believe that I can heal him?

THE FOUR MEN (*almost together*).   Of course, sir, we
    know you can. Who else could we go to? We believe in
    you. (*A moment's pause.*)

JESUS (*speaking to the paralyzed man*).   Look at me, my
    son—(*pause*)—your sins are forgiven!

(*An "Oh" of astonishment from the crowd.*)

1ST SCRIBE (*in a horrified whisper*).   But that's blasphemy!
    How dare he say that? Only God can forgive sins!

2ND SCRIBE (*scandalized*). I thought him a fine young man, but this is too much.

JESUS. I know exactly what you are thinking, you Scribes and Pharisees. Can a mere man cure paralysis, can a mere man forgive sins? Do you suppose one is any easier than the other? (*Pause*) Now I will prove to you that the Son of Man has full authority on earth to forgive sins.

(*He now speaks to paralytic.*)

My son, I have said that your sins are forgiven. Now rise, pick up that stretcher and walk home!

(*Gasp of astonishment.*)

ASSORTED VOICES (*amid excited hubbub*). Praise be to God, he's healed, he's walking!

A MAN'S VOICE (*emerging clearly from the crowd*). Stand back there! Let the lad go home. That was the hand of God, surely—praise God, I say!

(*Murmur of crowd rises.*)

WOMAN (*shouting from short distance outside*). God bless you, Master! We've never seen anything like this before.

(*Scene: Still inside, but fade out noise of crowd and footsteps.*)

1ST SCRIBE. Well, Ezra (*short pause*), as one Scribe to another, now that the mob has gone, what do you think of him?

2ND SCRIBE (*thoughtfully*). Frankly, I am in two minds about him. He spoke with authority, not like some of

our friends the Scribes. I could believe that he is a
prophet sent from God. But to forgive sins—(*Shud-
ders. Ugh!*) that sounds like blasphemy, or madness.

1ST SCRIBE. Blasphemy, but certainly not madness—the
man's as sane as you or I! But would God bless such
terrible presumption, Ezra?

2ND SCRIBE (*dryly*). Well, it appears that He did. (*Rather
hesitatingly*) Is it possible? . . . d'you think . . .
could this young man who called himself the Son of
Man possibly be—(*Pause*)—be the Messiah?

1ST SCRIBE. Ezra, you can't be serious! This young man
is Jesus of Nazareth, and everyone knows he is a
carpenter. But come, Ezra, we're letting ourselves be
overimpressed by what may have been lucky chance.

2ND SCRIBE. Perhaps. Let's go home now. (*Thoughtfully*)
We have certainly seen something extraordinary today.

⮞ 6 ⮜

THE HEALING AT THE POOL

OF BETHESDA

There was a feast of the Jews, and Jesus went up to Jerusalem. Now there is in Jerusalem near the sheep gate a pool surrounded by five arches which has a Hebrew name, Bethesda, meaning place of mercy. Under these arches a great many sick people were lying, waiting.

(Noise of approaching footsteps on stone.)

YOUNG MAN.   Is this the right place?

OLD CRIPPLE.   Right place for what, young man?

YOUNG MAN.   Well, I mean, is this Bethesda, the Place of Mercy? Everyone at home says that the waters of this pool have healing powers, at the right time, that is.

OLD CRIPPLE.   Ha! At the right time, he says! Listen, son, at certain times the water in that pool heaves and bubbles. Some say an angel touches it, but I don't know about that. All I know is that the first man in when it's bubbling gets cured. What's your trouble, chest, like me?

YOUNG MAN.   No, it's my arm, my right arm. Look at it. What good is a man with an arm like this?

OLD CRIPPLE.   Too bad, son. Still you'll have a good chance in the race, and what a race it is! (*Chuckles.*) Some hobbling, and some crawling, and a good deal of cursing and fighting going on. Of course, the lucky ones are the people who have a friend here at the right moment. Why, they'll pick you up, quick as lightning, and drop you in the pool and then all your troubles are over. (*Coughs distressingly.*)

YOUNG MAN.   But what happens if you can't move, and there's nobody to help you?

OLD CRIPPLE.   Well, I reckon you just stay here. (*Drops his voice.*) Come here. See that old fellow over there?

YOUNG MAN.   Yes.

OLD CRIPPLE.   We call him the Old-timer; been here thirty-eight years, they tell me. Can hardly move a muscle, wife's dead and he's got no friends here. But he's done pretty well out of it—half his mattress is filled with coins, so they say.

YOUNG MAN.   But doesn't anyone help the . . . Old-timer?

OLD CRIPPLE.   Not now they don't. He's got such a bitter tongue on him; lost his faith and spends his time cursing God. But who's this coming now? We don't often have visitors quite so early in the day. (*Lowers his voice.*) Look, he's making straight for the Old-timer. He's young to be one of his friends, and the poor old chap never had any sons—that I do know. Shsh!

JESUS.   My friend, you have been lying here for many years. I ask you one question. Do you *want* to get well again?

OLD-TIMER (*in rapid whining patter*).   Sir, you don't

understand my position. I can't move my legs. My wife's dead, and all my friends have left me. So when the angel touches the water in the pool, what chance have I got? It's not my fault . . .

JESUS (*commandingly*). Quiet. Get up, pick up that mattress and walk!

OLD-TIMER (*uncomprehendingly*). Me, me walk?

JESUS (*emphatically*). Yes, get up, pick up that mattress and walk!

OLD-TIMER (*his speech interspersed with groans*). I . . . can . . . move. Yes, I . . . can . . . pick up my mattress . . . (*Chanting exultantly*) I can walk, I can walk!

(*Pause. Street noises.*)

Oh, excuse me, Rabbi, I didn't mean to touch you, but you see I can walk!

1ST PHARISEE (*coldly*). And who told you, my man, that you could carry your bedding on the sabbath day? Have you forgotten the Law?

OLD-TIMER. Oh, I'm sorry, sir. But this has put everything out of my mind. You see, I've been lying helpless in the porches for thirty-eight years, and then a young man comes to me and he says, "Get up, pick up your mattress and walk!" And I did. It's like a new life.

1ST PHARISEE. Who was this young man?

OLD-TIMER. I don't know who he was, sir.

1ST PHARISEE. How did he dare to do any work himself, or make you work, on the holy sabbath?

OLD-TIMER. He seemed to speak . . . (*hesitatingly*) . . . with authority, and I just did as I was told. That's all.

1ST PHARISEE (*musingly*). A young man who seems to have authority, Reuben.

2ND PHARISEE. That sounds a little like our friend from Nazareth.

1ST PHARISEE. You, where did he go?

OLD-TIMER. I really couldn't tell you, sir. He just seemed to melt away into the crowd. He's probably still in the Temple somewhere.

1ST PHARISEE. Well, I must find him at once. This needs looking into!

(Goes off.)

OLD-TIMER *(to himself)*. Looking into, does it? *(Scornfully)* These Pharisees and their precious sabbath! But I'm well now, after thirty-eight years . . . *(in a burst of self-pity)* . . . thirty-eight years of misery. Oh, sir, you startled me!

JESUS. Look, you're a fit man now. Be careful you don't sin against God again, or you might find yourself worse off than you were before.

(Fade and Pause.)

(Subdued murmur of voices.)

2ND PHARISEE *(more reasonably)*. Are you sure it was this Jesus from Nazareth?

1ST PHARISEE. Well, here comes the young man in question, I think. *(Patronizingly)* Aren't you Jesus, the man from Nazareth?

JESUS. Yes, I am Jesus.

1ST PHARISEE *(harshly)*. But who exactly are you making yourself out to be?

2ND PHARISEE *(trying to be patient)*. Just a moment, EZRA. Young man, we're willing to be reasonable, but you'll get nowhere if you flout the Law—healing a man and telling him to carry his mattress on the sabbath!

JESUS. I tell you truly I am doing nothing of my own accord or on my own authority. But what the Father does I must do. The very deeds I am able to perform is your guarantee that the Father has sent me!

(*Murmurs of indignation.*)

2ND PHARISEE. Gently, gently, I feel sure he doesn't mean any blasphemy. Now, we know that God is our Father . . .

JESUS (*interrupting, with authority*). If God were really your Father, you would recognize me for the one I am. You would know that the Father has sent me to bring life to the world. I tell you truly the man who believes in me will not know death.

1ST PHARISEE (*at end of patience*). Young man, it's plain now that you're a raving lunatic! Abraham, Moses, the prophets, they all died. Are you claiming to be greater than they were?

JESUS. Your forefather Abraham died in the hope of seeing the day of the Son of Man. Now he has seen it and he is overjoyed.

(*Murmurs of indignation.*)

2ND PHARISEE (*still trying to be patient*). Look, my son, you're not fifty years old yet. Do you seriously mean us to believe that Abraham has seen *you?*

JESUS (*very solemnly*). I tell you that before there was an Abraham I AM.

ASSORTED ANGRY VOICES. That's utter blasphemy! Does he think he's God? This calls for strong action. Death to the man! Let me be the first to cast a stone at him.

At this they picked up stones to hurl at him, but Jesus hid himself and made his way out of the Temple.

∾ 7 ∾

THE HEALING OF THE MAN
BORN BLIND

(*Scene: The precincts of the Temple at Jerusalem—distant murmuring of people and cooing of doves.*)

1ST PHARISEE (*complacently*).   Another sabbath, and the end of another wonderful Festival here in Jerusalem! Have you not found it inspiring, Reuben, to have all these dear people of God worshiping Him in the Holy City?

2ND PHARISEE (*uncomfortably*).   Yes, but I've been profoundly disturbed by that young man Jesus from Nazareth.

1ST PHARISEE (*reassuringly*).   Disturbed? Oh, surely not! He's young and inexperienced and a bit of a rebel. He'll calm down all right. Anyway, I imagine he'll soon be on his way back to Galilee, and we shan't hear much more of him.

2ND PHARISEE (*still uncomfortably*).   I'm not so sure. Not many weeks ago, on a sabbath, he healed that man at the Pool of Bethesda.

1ST PHARISEE.   Yes, yes. But these enthusiasms pass, you know. What is more, he made such conceited answers

42

when he was reprimanded afterward that he nearly got himself stoned. That would be a fine thing to happen at the Festival.

2ND PHARISEE. I don't know, but the man bothers me. If he's proud and conceited, how could God heal a man through him, and on the sabbath day at that?

1ST PHARISEE. Proud he certainly is.

2ND PHARISEE (*doubtfully*). I suppose we are right in our views of, well, the sabbath, for instance?

1ST PHARISEE (*sharply*). Of course! The traditions of wise men are never wrong. And let me as an older man advise you, Reuben, that whatever your private feelings may be, never let anyone see them. Above all, never let the people know you have the faintest doubt about our authority.

(*A sound of excited voices is heard.*)

1ST VOICE. Rabbi! Rabbi!

1ST PHARISEE. Now what's this? This kind of noise is most unseemly in the Temple precincts on the sabbath!

2ND VOICE (*shouting*). Rabbi, we have a question for you!

1ST PHARISEE (*authoritatively*). Then let there be a seemly quietness. Let me remind you *all* that this is the sabbath.

1ST VOICE (*abashed*). We intend no irreverence, Rabbi, but we cannot help being excited. Look, here's a man we've all known as a beggar, blind from birth, and now, thanks to Jesus of Nazareth, he can see as well as any of us. This is what we want to ask you about.

2ND PHARISEE (*resignedly to himself*). I knew we should hear about that Jesus again. . . .

2ND VOICE. Well, I don't believe he's the same man as that beggar.

1ST VOICE.   If he isn't, it's his spit and image.

2ND VOICE.   Don't forget a pair of eyes makes a wonderful difference to a man's face!

MAN BORN BLIND. (*Who speaks throughout with a kind of exultant joy that makes him impervious to any criticism, and even makes him slightly impertinent*)   Of course, I'm the same man! I ought to know.

1ST PHARISEE (*sternly*).   Come now, I will not have all this shouting. All of you keep quiet—and let the man tell his own story.

MAN BORN BLIND.   Well, sir, it's perfectly simple. This man Jesus smeared some clay or something cool on my eyelids, told me to wash it off in the Pool of Siloam. I did and now I can see for the first time in my life! Praise God, I say!

1ST PHARISEE (*coldly*).   You realize that this deed was done on the sabbath, and that a man who breaks the sabbath is a sinner?

2ND PHARISEE (*half to himself*).   And yet he made a blind man see.

MAN BORN BLIND.   Sir, I can't see what all the fuss is about, honestly I can't. All my life I've been blind, now I can see. A few minutes ago some of your friends got hold of my father and mother to make sure I really was blind from birth. And they, bless them, said, "Well, ask the man himself. He's old enough to answer." They seemed kind of scared, but I'm not. I'm full of joy! It's marvelous to be able to see, marvelous!

1ST PHARISEE.   Now listen, you're quite right to give God the glory, but the man who's supposed to have done this thing, well, we know he's a sinner.

2ND PHARISEE (*wonderingly*).   But he healed you. Tell us what happened?

MAN BORN BLIND (*cheekily*). Why, weren't you listening? It's quite simple. He put clay on my eyes, I washed it off as he told me, and now I can see. That's all there is to it! But why all this curiosity? Are you wanting to follow him too, like so many others?

2ND PHARISEE. But did he really . . .

1ST PHARISEE (*interrupting harshly*). Reuben, I'll handle this. (*To the man*) That is sheer impertinence. We are followers of Moses. We know that God spoke to Moses, but as for this Jesus, some young preacher up from the country, what do we know of him?

MAN BORN BLIND (*amused*). Well, here's an extraordinary thing! It's never been heard of before for a man born blind to be healed! And all you can say about the man who did it is that he's a sinner, and that you know practically nothing about him. Why, even I know that a sinner couldn't get this power from God. God would only work such a miracle through a very good man. I am convinced he's not only a very good man—he's a prophet!

1ST PHARISEE (*exploding with fury*). You unspeakable scoundrel! Born in sin and dirt, are *you* attempting to teach *us*, the appointed guardians of the Truth of God? Be off with you, you and your friends! How dare you defile the Temple with your blasphemy, with your insolence! You are here and now expelled from the Temple of God!

Jesus heard that the Pharisees had expelled the man born blind, and he sought him out.

MAN BORN BLIND (*reverently, half to himself*). Dear God, what a day it's been, and here I rest for a moment on

my way home. I hope my friends didn't mind my sending them all away, but I had to be alone—alone to
thank God, and alone to think out my life afresh.

JESUS (*gently*).   You are not alone, my friend.

MAN BORN BLIND.   The Prophet!

JESUS.   When I heard that you had been expelled from the
Temple, I came to find you.

MAN BORN BLIND (*startled*).   If you only knew what
you've done for me today! I praise God with the whole
of my being that I can see; no more need for begging,
I can work like other men. I don't mind being expelled
from the Temple. If they don't recognize a good man
like you they're the ones who are blind, not me.

JESUS (*with gentle emphasis*).   Do you believe in—
(*pause*)—the Son of God?

MAN BORN BLIND (*eagerly*).   I would like to sir. But who
is he?

JESUS.   You have seen him with your newly opened eyes,
and he is talking to you now.

MAN BORN BLIND.   You? Lord, I believe! And I gladly give
you the worship and love of all my heart!

JESUS.   It is strange, my friend, that I the Son of God have
come into the world to save the world and yet my
coming judges it. For those who were blind have their
eyes opened and see who I am, but those who think
they have seen the Truth are blind and do not see the
Son of God, though he is here before their eyes.

8

JESUS RETURNS TO GALILEE

(Scene: Back in Galilee by the lakeside.)

PETER *(with a sigh of content)*.   Master, it's good to have you back with us here in Galilee.

JESUS *(kindly)*.   Thank you, Simon, but what have you all been doing while I've been on my Father's business in Jerusalem? You tell me, Andrew.

ANDREW *(a little mournfully)*.   Well, Master, we've been wandering about like sheep without a shepherd. Of course, we've been thinking and talking about the Kingdom, as you told us, and we've done a little praying, but none of us seems to know much about it.

JESUS.   And what about you, Matthew? Did you feel I'd deserted you?

MATTHEW *(with quick loyalty)*.   Of course not, Master. The moment I met you I knew you had a purpose for me. I knew you hadn't called me from my tax collecting for nothing! I've needed this time of quiet to get myself sorted out and make myself as ready as I can for the new life.

JESUS.   Yes, Matthew! And James and John, how have you two spent your time?

JAMES (*a bit disappointed with himself*). Well, we've been trying to do something for the Kingdom. We've been around to some of the villages, trying to tell them about you, and about the Kingdom, and how you'd called us to help.

JESUS. And you, John?

JOHN (*fed up*). We weren't very good at it, I must say. I thought it would be easy after John the Baptist's preaching and all the good you've done, Master, to persuade people to join with us in building the Kingdom of God here and now.

JAMES. Yes, and it would be easy if it weren't for the stupidity, the blindness, the pigheadedness of some of these villagers!

JOHN. Why, you could talk for hours and hours and they'd just sit there, smiling and nodding their heads. And then, at the end, you'd find they'd learnt precisely nothing.

JAMES. Sometimes I feel I could wring their silly necks.

JESUS. Yes, James and John, but the Kingdom of God will never be built by giving way to anger or impatience. Think, all of you, of our heavenly Father. He makes the sun shine on all men, rich and poor, clever and stupid, good and bad. When He sends rain it falls on the good man and on the bad alike. His love goes out to the ungrateful and to the evil, and this is the sort of love you must have if you are to build the Kingdom with me.

PETER (*warningly*). Master, people are beginning to collect round us. Is that all right?

ANDREW. People! There are *crowds* coming from all directions. Does it matter, Master?

JESUS. Not a bit, Andrew. You can see how great is the harvest; it is the laborers who are so few. Let me invite them closer. Come near, my friends, come all of you who are weary and overburdened. Come to me and hear my message; it will be rest and relief to your souls.

You are all so anxious, weighed down with the burdens of tomorrow which need never be carried today. I tell you, you are in the hand of your heavenly Father, and there is no need for your anxiety; He knows your needs, for you are all His children. I tell you to put first His Kingdom and His goodness, and everything else will come to you as a matter of course.

Look at the birds in the sky—(*Half humorously*) not one of them sows or reaps or stores his food in a barn. Yet your heavenly Father feeds them. And look round at the flowers of the field, yes at the very grass on which you're sitting. They neither work nor weave, yet I tell you that not even Solomon in all his glory was arrayed like one of these. Now, if your heavenly Father gives so much care to the beauty of these flowers which bloom in the fields today and tomorrow may be dry and burned to bake your bread, how much more is He concerned to clothe you, His children? And never worry about tomorrow! One day's trouble is enough for one day and tomorrow can look after itself.

And all the people were attentive to hear him. And it came to pass in those days that Jesus went up into a mountain to pray, and continued all night in prayer to God. And when it was day he called unto him his disciples.

(*It is early morning on the hillside.*)

JESUS. I have called you Twelve here away from the crowds for a special reason.

VOICE.   Yes, Master.

JESUS.   I have already spoken of the laborers in the harvest, and you Twelve are the first laborers my Father has sent me. Simon and Andrew, I called you from your fishing, and you came gladly. And you, too, James and John, I called to be fishers of men.

PETER.   } *(speaking* } Yes, we left it all to follow you.
JOHN.   } *almost* } Yes, indeed we will, Master.
ANDREW. } *together)* } That's true, Master.
JAMES.   } We'll do more than talk, Master.

JESUS.   And then, Philip and Bartholomew, I called you too; I made it no secret that to follow me may be both costly and dangerous.

PHILIP and BARTHOLOMEW *(together)*.   Yes, Master, we understand that.

JESUS.   And then, Matthew, you came, and I know that your heart is changing already. When you sat at your tax collecting you had money but you had little love; I offer you no money but much love.

MATTHEW.   Thank you, Master. I'll do whatever you say.

JESUS.   And Thomas—*(teasingly)* still not quite sure why you answered my call? Believe me, Thomas, the time will come when you will be very sure.

THOMAS *(woodenly)*.   Yes, Master.

JESUS.   James, son of Alphaeus and Mary, you may be short in inches but already you see far over the heads of men taller than you.

JAMES *(a little overcome)*.   Thank you, Master.

JESUS.   And then you, Judas, son of James, and your friend, Simon the Canaanite, both of you burning with passion for this land of our fathers. I need men of zeal, but I call you to strive for a Kingdom not of this world.

JUDAS AND SIMON (*together*). We'll follow you anywhere
Master.

JESUS. And last of my Twelve, you Judas Iscariot, the only
man among us not a Galilean, you came many miles
from the south of Judaea to seek and find me. Judas,
in me and my Kingdom you may see the true fulfill-
ment of your dreams.

JUDAS. That is my hope, Master.

JESUS (*seriously*). You Twelve I have chosen, and I now
appoint you my Apostles, my Special Messengers.
Sometimes you will be at my side, watching and learn-
ing the ways of the Kingdom. Sometimes I shall send
you out in my name to do my work. When I send you
out you shall have a power greater than your own. You
are to heal the sick, to cleanse the lepers, to cast out
the evil spirits that torture men's minds.

I send you out as sheep among wolves, for men are
dangerous. At all times you are to trust in the Father
and reverence Him alone. (*A pause—bird song is
heard.*) Remember the birds of the air. Some men,
alas, cage them and so little do they value them that
two sparrows are sold for a farthing, and yet not one
of these little creatures falls to the ground without my
Father's knowledge. So you, my beloved Twelve,
never be afraid. You are worth more than a great
many sparrows. You are always in the Father's care,
and in His eyes even the hairs on your head are all
numbered!

◈ 9 ◈

THE LORD'S PRAYER

(Scene: in a desert place.)

PETER *(sighs)*.   Oh, what a relief to get away from people, even though we do have to trudge out into the desert to get a bit of peace. Phew! I've never seen such crowds! How did you feel about them, Matthew?

MATTHEW.   Well, Simon, I'm certainly used to people, and crowds never used to bother me. But these crowds have been different. They're so demanding. The Master must be absolutely worn out.

PETER.   Yes, he is. He's gone off up the valley to pray.

JAMES.   I only hope he's somewhere out of the sun. He's been giving out, day after day—healing, comforting, answering those clever fellows they sent down from Jerusalem, not to speak of the scores of times he's preached about the Kingdom. Sometimes the people make me downright angry.

MATTHEW.   They take advantage of the Master's kindness, and many of them never so much as give him a "thank you" afterward.

PETER. And now he's gone off to pray. Personally, I'd be much too tired for that.

JUDAS (*firmly*). But he gets his strength from prayer, that's plain.

PETER. Why, Judas, you startled me! I thought you were asleep in the shade of this rock like all the rest.

JUDAS (*wearily*). I have slept because my body needs sleep. I wish it didn't. I've never seen a man like the Master. He seems made of iron. I'd like to know just what goes on when he prays.

MATTHEW. And so would I. I certainly can't imagine *him* praying long prayers out loud for the sake of effect. (*Reminiscently*) How often I used to see Pharisees doing that at street corners!

JUDAS (*as though the others have not spoken*). I think it's his *will* that gets strengthened. I've no use for pious platitudes, little prayers to keep on the right side of God, or requests to the Almighty for things we could perfectly well do for ourselves. But the weakness of all men lies in the will, and that's where the Master gets his strength.

JAMES. I believe he's on his way back to us now. I just saw his cloak up there among the rocks. (*Pause.*) Yes, he's moving toward us.

JUDAS. That means in a few minutes he'll be here. And what shall we see? A man worn out, and looking as though he's spent all night repeating meaningless phrases? No. We shall see a man, tired maybe, but a man renewed inside, and the new strength will shine in his eyes. (*With sudden vehemence*) I tell you there's *nothing* this man cannot do.

PETER. Well, why don't we ask him how to pray?

MATTHEW.   Yes, why not? I certainly know there's a God,
and when I do pray I know He hears me.

JUDAS (*slowly and almost greedily*).   I'd give anything to
know the secret of his power.

PETER (*enthusiastically*).   What's wrong with waking the
others up, and asking the Master to give us all a lesson?
(*He calls.*) Come on, Andrew, wake up! Simon, James,
John, all of you—time to get up, the Master's coming
back!

(*A short pause, with a few yawns as the disciples awake.*)

JESUS.   Peace be with you, my friends, on this lovely morning!

ASSORTED VOICES OF DISCIPLES.   Peace with you, Master!
Greetings to you!

PETER.   Master, come and sit with us in the shade of this
great rock, and the rest of you, gather round. There's
room for us all. (*Fussily as they settle down*) No,
James, that's the Master's place. Matthew, you move
up a bit and make room for Simon. Now get comfortable, all of you.

(*A moment's pause with some noise of shuffling garments.*)

JUDAS.   Now that we're settled, Master, we have a request
to make of you.

JESUS.   Well, Judas?

JUDAS (*deliberately*).   We want you to teach us to pray.

PETER (*eagerly*).   Yes, Master. John taught his disciples
after his fashion. Now we want you, the Master, to tell
us how it's done.

JESUS.   How it's done, Simon? Do you think I have some
magic spell to give you?

PETER (*embarrassed*).   Master, I didn't mean it like that.

JAMES.   When we were children, we all learned to say our prayers, but we haven't learned to pray as grown-up men.

PETER.   Will you teach us how we ought to pray, Master?

JESUS.   I pray to my Father and your Father. I pray where I can be alone and quiet and remember the Father's presence. (*Pause.*) You have been taught since childhood that your heavenly Father knows what you need before you ask.

PETER.   I know, Master. Of course, He must.

MATTHEW.   But when I try to pray, Master, I keep thinking of my sins and my failures. I can't seem to get past them.

JUDAS (*forcefully*).   When *I* pray to almighty God, I see before me what I might be, what I might accomplish. I seek the power to make those dreams come true!

JESUS (*with gentle authority*).   My disciples, listen to me. I will give you a pattern of prayer. I will say it slowly. It may surprise you—indeed, it may puzzle you. But as you have often heard me say, the man who has ears to hear should use them. This then is your pattern.

(*He speaks slowly and deliberately, with a pause after each phrase.*)

Our heavenly Father,
May your Name be honored,
May your Kingdom come,
And may your Will be done on earth, as it is in Heaven;
Give us each day the bread that we need;
Forgive us our offenses against you, just as we forgive those who offend against us;
Do not lead us into temptation, but save us from the evil one;

For the Kingdom is yours, the Power is yours and the
Glory is yours for all eternity,   Amen.

THE TWELVE (*not quite all together*).   Amen.

(*There is a moment's pause. Then* PETER, *finding the
silence unbearable, speaks.*)

PETER.   Well, Master, that sounds simple enough.

JUDAS (*scornfully*).   Simple? It's nothing of the kind.
Can't you see there's a whole new way of living in
that, perhaps a whole new power? I must go off alone
and think. Master, may I go?

JESUS.   Yes, Judas. And God go with you.

MATTHEW (*a little hesitantly*).   I didn't quite understand
that piece about forgiveness, Master.

PETER (*naïvely*).   Yes, just how often have we got to forgive people? Would seven times be enough as a gen-
eral rule?

JESUS (*gently*).   No, Simon, and neither would seventy
times seven! You are to forgive others as freely and as
generously as your heavenly Father forgives you.
(*More seriously*) Indeed, I tell you all that unless you
forgive your brother fully and freely for whatever
wrongs he has done to you, neither will your Father
forgive you the wrongs you have done against Him.

JAMES (*thoughtfully*).   That's a hard thing to say.

JESUS.   Yes, the Kingdom of God calls for many things
that seem hard to men. But let me go carefully through
the pattern again. And then we will talk of it together.
Listen once more. Our heavenly Father, May your
Name be honored, May your Kingdom come . . .
(*voice of* JESUS *fades*).

❧ 10 ❧

THE CENTURION'S SERVANT

When Jesus had ended all his sayings in the audience of the people, he entered into Capernaum. And a certain centurion's servant, who was dear to him, was sick and ready to die.

(Scene: Roman barracks at Capernaum.)

ROMAN SOLDIER *(gruffly, but kindly)*.   What's the matter, lad—feeling miserable? Capernaum's a long way from Rome. But you'll be going back there next leave, never fear.

BOY.   Oh, I'm all right, soldier.

ROMAN SOLDIER.   And there's many worse places than Capernaum, believe me, The people here don't give us Romans much trouble, the food's good, there's plenty of sunshine, and you might say this is a health resort. And when you're off duty, there's always sailing and fishing on the lake. *And,* I reckon we've got just about the best centurion over us in the whole army. Mind you, he's strict. "Do this," he says, and you do it, or else. "Come here," he says, and you come at once, if

57

you know what's good for you. If you obey orders,
he's a proper gentleman—couldn't wish for a better.
BOY (*enthusiastically*).   Oh, I know. I think he's the most
wonderful soldier I've ever known. But I can't bear
to see him so . . .
ROMAN SOLDIER.   So upset, you mean? He's taking it really
hard about this servant of his. Of course he's been with
him for years and become more like a son than a
servant. And now, they say he's likely to die at any
minute. Ah well, that's life, that is. (*He whistles tune-
lessly.*)
ANOTHER ROMAN SOLDIER (*bursting in*).   Boy!
BOY (*eagerly*).   Yes, sir.
2ND ROMAN SOLDIER (*urgently*).   Take an urgent message
for the centurion.
BOY.   For the centurion? Oh, yes, sir.
2ND ROMAN SOLDIER (*in clipped military tones*).   Right,
well listen carefully. You know the centurion's servant
is ill, very ill.
BOY.   Yes, sir.
2ND ROMAN SOLDIER.   Now we've just heard that Jesus of
Nazareth has arrived here in Capernaum. Your job's
to run to the town and find some of the Jewish elders.
Get them to appeal to this Jesus to heal the young
man.
BOY.   You mean bring Jesus all the way up here?
2ND ROMAN SOLDIER.   Not necessary. Centurion's orders
are simply to get Jesus to give the command. He's convinced that's all that's required. Got it? You persuade
the elders to get Jesus to give that order. But, hurry,
there's no time to lose!
BOY.   Right, sir. I'll run all the way.

(Scene: A street in Capernaum.)

1ST ELDER. I hear Jesus of Nazareth has come back to our city. What a reputation that young man has got! You and I, as elders of the Synagogue, have to be pretty cautious, but to hear the people talk, you'd think he could do anything.

2ND ELDER (*dryly*). Except in Nazareth, I hear. Apparently they gave him a pretty rough time. They don't like their young carpenter turning into a prophet.

1ST ELDER. Well, that's their loss. It's probably the old story of the prophet having no honor among his own countrymen.

2ND ELDER. But no one could deny his powers here in Capernaum. Why, last time he was here I saw sick people healed with my own eyes!

1ST ELDER. Even the Pharisees down here from Jerusalem couldn't deny that he really did heal people.

2ND ELDER. No, they couldn't deny it. But did you hear them saying quite openly that he was doing it because he was in league with Satan?

1ST ELDER (*chuckles reminiscently*). I certainly did, and I heard his answer! "Could Satan be divided against himself?" he said. "Did they really imagine that Satan could do God's work?" And then he added, "Oh, no, a house divided against itself wouldn't last long."

2ND ELDER. Yes, the Pharisees are getting more and more divided themselves, you know. Some of them would give a good deal to get this Jesus quietly put out of the way. But others are not so sure; they can't help recognizing the good he's doing—in spite of some of the extraordinary things he says.

1ST ELDER. Hm! That's rather what I feel myself, you know. All this power of doing good and healing disease must come from God. But when he starts talking as though he's on special terms with the Lord God, well, to say the least, I feel extremely uncomfortable.

(*Sound of approaching running footsteps.*)

Hello, who's this? Looks like one of the Roman lads from the barracks, and in a tearing hurry.

BOY. Sirs, I have an urgent order from the centurion!

1ST ELDER. Order, eh? Look, boy, we're Jewish elders, not Roman soldiers!

BOY. I'm sure I beg your pardon, sirs. It's an order to me, but it's a request to you. His servant's terribly ill—he may die at any moment. The centurion says will you ask Jesus just to give the order to have his servant healed. Oh, please come—Jesus is only in the next street.

1ST ELDER. This is very strange!

2ND ELDER. Well, your centurion's a good friend of ours, and we don't mind putting in a word for him, though Heaven knows whether it will make any difference.

BOY. Oh, thank you, thank you, sirs. But please hurry, he's only just round the corner.

(*Fade out on footsteps.*)

(*Fade in on crowd background noise.*)

1ST ELDER (*hurriedly*). Jesus of Nazareth, this is no time for formalities. We are elders of the Synagogue here—

JESUS. Well, my friend?

1ST ELDER. We come to ask you to use the powers which God has given you to heal the servant of our centurion. By all accounts he is desperately ill.

2ND ELDER. I add my plea to that. This Roman is no ordinary Gentile. He's a man who worships the true God. He's been more than fair toward us Jews. He even built our Synagogue out of his own pocket. And now apparently he's quite certain that you can heal his servant.

JESUS. Quite certain?

BOY. Oh, quite, quite certain, sir. He says you've only to speak the word, you needn't even come to the house. He wouldn't think the barracks a fit place for you, sir.

JESUS. All the same, we will go to him. (*Pause.*) But wait, who's this, another messenger?

BOY. Oh, sir, I do hope he hasn't come to tell us it's too late.

2ND ROMAN SOLDIER. Master, there is no need for you to take a step farther. The centurion has just sent me down to stop you. He's a trained soldier, and he says that you have only to give the order and he knows that his servant will be perfectly well. To him it's as simple as that.

JESUS (*wonderingly*). To him it is as simple as that! And indeed, so it is. Everything is possible to the man who really believes. Yet I tell you, my friends, I have never found faith as great as this, even among God's people Israel. I tell you that there will be many more men of faith from among the Gentiles. They will come from the east and from the west, and they will take their place with Abraham and Isaac and Jacob in the Kingdom of God. Now go back to your friend the centurion and tell him this from me: "As you have believed, so shall it be done for you."

And his servant was healed in the selfsame hour.

∞ 11 ∞

CHRIST THE SON OF GOD

Jesus cometh to Bethsaida; and they bring a blind man unto him, and besought him to touch him. And Jesus took the blind man by the hand, and led him out of the town.

BLIND MAN. Master, where have you taken me?

JESUS. Do you not trust me?

BLIND MAN. Oh, indeed, Master! We blind people can tell a lot by touch. Your hand is kind and firm. I know you are good.

JESUS. Well, keep still now and go on trusting me. We are in the fields away from the crowds. Only a few of my friends are here.

BLIND MAN. I will do whatever you say. (*Exclaims*) Oh, your hands are cool on my eyelids! Now my eyes are tingling. (*Excitedly*) Something is trying to break through.

JESUS. Now I take my hands away. Open your eyes! Tell me what has happened to you.

BLIND MAN (*tremblingly*). Oh, oh! I think . . . I . . . can . . . see! It is all so bright! This must be grass, yes, grass that I have so often felt through my sandals and touched with my hands. I can see trunks of trees,

but—(*alarmed*)—oh! they are walking about like
men. This is too much! I feel confused. . . .

JESUS.   I will put my hands on your eyes again.

BLIND MAN (*rather frightened and breathless*).   Yes,
Master.

JESUS.   Keep still and trust me; feel my hands again.
(*Pause.*) Now look! What do you see now?

BLIND MAN (*rapturously*).   Oh, everything, everything,
bright and clear! The blue of God's sky which men
have told me about, which I have never seen. The
flowers in the grass at my feet, all lovelier than I had
ever thought. And people, Master, people with kind
faces, and smiles in their eyes. Oh, it is too much! But
praise God, praise God! I can see! I can see!

JESUS.   Yes, praise God indeed, but now go to your own
home. I do not want you to say anything to people in
the village. As for me and my followers, we will take
the road to the north.

BLIND MAN (*rapturously*).   Yes, Master, I will do just as
you say! I feel I can never stop thanking God, the God
who can even make the blind to see!

And Jesus went forth, and his disciples, into the villages of
Caesarea Philippi.

(*Scene: on the road to Caesarea Philippi*)

PETER (*grumbling good-humoredly*).   Andrew, I wonder
why we have to trudge through all these villages?

ANDREW.   I honestly don't know, Simon, but I'm sure the
Master does. Sometimes he frightens me. He seems to
be following a plan we know nothing about.

PETER.   He makes me feel very small, Andrew. (*Wryly*)

We get worried and then he smiles and calls us men of little faith for being so anxious! But after all, we're only human. But Andrew, I'm beginning to think he's someone much more than human.

ANDREW.   I know. How could a mere man feed that huge crowd yesterday? Why, there must have been five thousand men, let alone their wives and children! And they all had plenty to eat.

PETER.   Yes, and how could a mere man make a blind man see, but it happened today. And yet . . . well, look at him now, walking ahead with James and John and talking to them. He looks just like the rest of us.

ANDREW.   Ah, but when you hear him talking . . .

PETER (*interrupting*).   Well, come on then, let's catch up. (*Short pause*) We'll hear what he's saying now! Come on, Andrew.

JESUS.   Well, my friends, we are nearly there. Sit down, all of you, under the shade of this tree. (*Audible response.*) I have a question to ask. (*Pause.*) (*Very deliberately*) Who do men say that I am?

ANDREW.   Some say you're John the Baptist come back from the dead.

JUDAS.   Well, *I've* heard people say you're Jeremiah. But that's nonsense. You're a greater man than Jeremiah ever was!

ANDREW.   Well, most people seem pretty certain that you're one of the old prophets come to life again.

JESUS (*quietly*).   But who do you say that I am?

PETER (*exultantly*).   You are Christ, the Son of the living God!

JESUS.   Bless you, Simon, Son of Jonah. No *man* could have told you that truth but only my Father who is in heaven. From now on, I shall call you Peter—a Rock.

PETER (*abashed*). O Master, you know how weak and foolish I am. . . .

JESUS. But I will make you firm and steady as a Rock. (*To disciples.*) Now, remember all of you, do not breathe a word of this truth to anyone.

ANDREW. No, Master.

(*Disciples' murmured response.*)

JESUS. For I tell you that much suffering lies in the path of the Son of Man. The elders, the chief priests and the scribes will all spurn and reject him. In the end their hatred will kill him. Nevertheless, in three days he will rise again!

PETER (*horrified*). Master, Lord! You *must not* talk of things like that. Such things must never happen to the Holy One, the Christ of God . . .

JESUS (*sternly*). Peter, those are the words of Satan himself. You speak like the enemy. Would you tempt the Son of Man from the path he must follow? Your mind is filled with thoughts of man's success and man's glory, and you have forgotten the glory of God. The Son must do the will of the Father, whatever the cost. (*Pause.*) Indeed, I tell you that if any of you would be a true follower of mine, he must forget about himself, and take up his cross and follow me.

JUDAS (*gruffly*). Master, I do not understand. Do you mean that a follower of yours must give up everything, and lose all that is precious to him?

JESUS. I tell you that the man who wants to save his life must first lose it. And yet whoever loses his life for my sake will find it.

JUDAS. Master, I still do not understand. If we are to give up, and throw away, and lose, what is there to gain?

JESUS (*deliberately*).   What good is it to a man if he gains everything in the whole world and loses his own soul? What could a man give to get back his own soul once he has lost it?

~ 12 ~

THE TRANSFIGURATION

Jesus said, I tell you of a truth, there be some standing here, who shall not taste of death, till they see the kingdom of God. And it came to pass about eight days after these sayings, that he took Peter and John and James, and went up into a mountain to pray.

JAMES (*in an urgent whisper*). John, are you awake?

JOHN. Yes, James, something woke me up a few minutes ago.

JAMES. Can you see what's happening to the Master?

JOHN (*astonished and awed*). Where? There's a bright light shining on him! It's not just the sunlight. I think we ought to wake Peter.

JAMES (*again in urgent whisper*). Yes—Peter, Peter, wake up!

PETER (*drowsily*). Er . . . what is it? I'm sleepy.

JAMES. So were John and I. But something's happened to the Master.

PETER (*waking up*). Happened to the Master? (*Yawns*) What could happen to him up here? He went farther up the mountain to pray. But (*in sudden alarm*) d'you mean there's been an accident, James? Has he slipped or fallen?

JAMES.   No, no, nothing like that. But do keep your voice down.

PETER.   Why?

JOHN.   Peter, the Master didn't bring the three of us up here just to sleep. We could have done that in the valley.

JAMES.   I believe he wanted us to see something, something wonderful.

JOHN.   Look up there! Up there at the summit of the mountain. Look at that strange bright light shining on him!

PETER (*impatiently*).   Yes, yes, I can see it, and the Master. At first I thought it was some trick of the sunlight and the mist, but it's far brighter than that. (*Excitedly, as a sudden thought strikes him*) Wait a minute, d'you remember what he said a few days ago—some of us would not die until we had seen the Kingdom of God come with power? D'you think he's invited us three up here to see something like that?

JAMES.   Well, it would certainly be like him.

JOHN.   Yes, I agree, though I don't understand. Why, when you realized the other day, Peter, who he really was, he told us all to keep silent.

PETER.   Yes, yes, but it would still be like him, don't you see? He tells the crowd about the Kingdom, he heals the sick and does all kinds of good things, but when it comes to who he really is, it's only us Twelve who are told anything about it. Yes, that's probably why . . .

JAMES (*impatiently*).   Oh, be quiet, Peter, and just look. (*Wonderingly.*) Oh!

(*Pause.*)

PETER (*strongly moved*). Yes, that's not sunlight. That's the very light of Heaven! Oh, he's changing before our eyes. He's the same Jesus we know and follow . . . and yet his face is different. It's the face of a king . . . a wonderful . . . glorious . . . king!

JOHN (*awed*). Yes, this must be what he's like all the time. Oh, dear God, we are seeing the King in his glory.

JAMES. The light, the light—it hurts my eyes! And yet I cannot look away. Even his robes dazzle me.

JOHN. He's not alone now. There are two other shining figures with him. Who can they be? Angels of light?

PETER. No, I know who they are. One's Moses and one's Elijah, and they're bowing low before him.

JAMES. Of course, of course. Oh, what a sight! This is the beginning of the Kingdom coming in glory!

(*Music.*)

Don't you see it's the Law and Prophets bearing witness to the Son of God?

PETER. Yes, and now they seem to be talking to him. I can't hear what they're saying, can you?

(*Music.*)

JAMES (*awe struck*). I don't understand this. I'm frightened!

PETER (*with sudden almost hysterical boldness*). Nonsense! We were invited here. I wouldn't miss it for the world. (*He calls.*) Master, this is a wonderful experience for us! Couldn't we stay up here? We could easily put up three shelters for you, and Moses and Elijah.

JOHN (*more frightened at Peter's boldness*). Peter, be quiet! You don't know what you're saying. But look out, that bright cloud is rolling down toward us! I'm afraid. Get down on your knees and cover your faces, you two. There's too much light!

JAMES. Cover your face, Peter!

PETER (*wondering and abashed*). Yes, yes, I will, and bow my head to the ground.

(*Music.*)

But I meant no harm—I'm only a sinful man who was overjoyed to see the Master's glory. . . .

(*His voice fades. Music. Pause.*)

JESUS. Peter, James, John, open your eyes and get up now. There is nothing to fear. There is no one here but me.

PETER. Oh, Master, we can never forget what we have just seen.

JAMES AND JOHN (*together*). No, never.

PETER. But, Master, surely it *was* Moses and Elijah we saw standing there and talking to you? It was wonderful, I wished it could last forever!

JAMES (*interrupting*). But the light was too much for us, Master. Our eyes were dazzled by the brightness of your glory.

JOHN. And we couldn't hear what Moses and Elijah were saying.

PETER. Well, at least I could see that they seemed very serious, and yet afterward they smiled at you, Master.

JESUS. Indeed they were serious, Peter. They spoke of the way the Son of Man must take. They spoke of rejection and betrayal, of suffering, pain and death.

(*A pause.*) And then they talked of how the Father would raise the Son from the dead! It was then I think that they smiled.

PETER (*shakily*). Must all this happen to you, Master? Is there no hope, is there no other way?

JESUS. The Son of Man must tread the path the Father has set before him. The Law and the Prophets foretell his suffering, and the men in Jerusalem will assuredly fulfill those prophecies. It is in the city that the Son of Man must be condemned to death. (*Pause.*) You, Peter, James and John, have seen what no man has ever seen, but you are to tell nobody about it until the Son of Man is risen from the dead.

The Transfiguration

❧ 13 ❧

THE JOURNEY TO JERUSALEM

And it came to pass, when the time was come that Jesus should be received up, he steadfastly set his face to go to Jerusalem.

PETER (*gloomily*). I don't like this, Andrew, I don't like it at all.

ANDREW. Tired of walking, Peter? I admit this dust makes it pretty hard going. I never did like this road to Samaria. Oh, that's another stone got into my sandal.

PETER. No, of course it's not the walk, though I don't like the dust and heat any more than you do.

ANDREW (*easing out pebble*). Ah, that's got it out. What is it then, Peter?

PETER. It's that set look on the Master's face as he strides on there ahead, and all that talk we've been hearing recently about meeting his death in Jerusalem. It makes me feel cold all over, in spite of the sun.

ANDREW. I know what you mean, Peter, but soon we'll be joined by hundreds of others going up to the Passover. Why, nobody would dare to do anything against the Master with thousands of people solidly behind him, surely?

PETER (*gloomily*). Well, I don't know. It doesn't feel like an ordinary Passover journey to me. Why, for instance, have we got to go through Samaria? I heard the Master send James and John ahead to get lodgings for us there. Oh, hello, Judas!

JUDAS. Hello, Andrew.

ANDREW. What do you think about this journey?

JUDAS (*enthusiastically*). I believe this is going to be something rather spendid. All this time spent in little towns and villages is all very well, but if you really want something done, you've got to go to the heart of things, to the leaders, to the city itself. And what better time could you have than the Passover? There'll be thousands of people supporting him, and now, if ever, is the time when he should show himself as the King!

PETER. I hope you're right. But from one or two things he's said, you'd think he was going to his death.

JUDAS. Well, it's very serious for him, of course, and no great leader is quite like ordinary men. I'm not surprised he's tense. There may be danger, but he's the man to face it. You'll see, it'll be a triumph!

ANDREW. I hope so. Hello, here comes James and John! Oh, they've had bad news judging from the look on their faces. They're going straight to the Master. Let's catch up so that we can hear what they've got to say.

JAMES (*indignantly*). Master, they won't have us in Samaria!

JOHN (*furiously*). We've never been so insulted in our lives! I never had much love for Samaritans, but this is the limit!

JESUS. What reason did they give?

JAMES. Oh, they made the excuse that we're plainly making for Jerusalem.

JOHN. They won't let Jews set foot inside their precious houses, especially at Passover time.

JAMES. Master, it's the crowning insult!

JOHN. Here are you, the King, as we all know, and these dogs of Samaritans won't give us a bed for the night.

JAMES. Shall we curse them, shall we call down fire from Heaven as Elijah did and burn up their squalid little villages?

JESUS. James, John, my sons of thunder! What sort of spirit is that for the followers of the Kingdom to show? Have you forgotten that the Son of Man has not come to destroy men's lives, but to save them? Indeed, he came not to be served but to serve, and to give his life as a ransom for many. (*Pause.*) Come, all of you, we will take the other road and join the crowds as they journey to Jerusalem.

And it came to pass, as they went in the way, a great multitude followed them.

(*Murmur of crowds in the background.*)

PETER. Listen, Master, this feels more like old times. It's good to feel that our little band's among the thousands going up to the Passover.

JESUS (*solemnly*). Yes, yes, it is good, Peter, and yet I say again to all of you Twelve that everything prophesied about the Son of Man will come true. He will be handed over to the Gentiles, he will be jeered at and insulted and finally put to death. But I tell you truly that on the third day he will rise again.

PETER. Master, none of this seems to make sense to us. Look how the people love you and follow you! Why, here comes one of our rulers, a very rich young man, everyone says. Surely, he's no enemy of yours?

RICH YOUNG RULER (*with warm enthusiasm*). Good Master, what must I do to live with God forever when I die?

JESUS (*musingly*). I wonder what makes you call me good? God is the only one who is good. But you know the commandments. Do not commit adultery; do not kill; do not steal; do not bear false witness; honor your father and your mother.

RICH YOUNG RULER (*eagerly*). Yes, I know the commandments, and I have kept them all since I was quite young.

JESUS. I can see that, but there is one thing you have missed—(*challengingly*). Sell everything that you possess and give the money away to the poor and you will find true riches in Heaven. And then come and follow me!

(*Pause.*)

RICH YOUNG RULER (*devastated*). But, but Master, that needs thinking about. I have my position to consider. It isn't as simple as all that . . . (*Voice trails off.*) It needs thinking about.

(*Pause.*)

JESUS. See how he leaves us, dragging his footsteps. How different a few moments ago when he was all eagerness and willingness to serve. Alas, how hard, how very hard it is for a wealthy man to enter the Kingdom. (*With wry humor.*) You know, it would be easier to squeeze a camel through the eye of a needle than to get a rich man through the gates of the Kingdom! I

tell you that unless a man is prepared to give up all
that he has to follow me he can never be my disciple.

JOHN (*amazed*).　But who then can possibly be saved?

JESUS.　Things that you may think impossible are possible
with God. Never forget that with God all things are
possible.

JOHN (*almost tearfully*).　Master, you make it all seem so
hard! People go away discouraged.

JESUS.　I know, John. The way does seem hard.

PETER.　Every one of us has left everything to follow you.

JESUS.　Yes, Peter. I tell you that every man who leaves his
home, or his loved ones, when I call him to work for
the kingdom, will certainly receive far more than he
gave up, even in this present world, and in the world
beyond he shall share the very life of God.

THE PARABLE OF THE PHARISEE
AND THE TAX COLLECTOR

(*Scene: Road to Jerusalem, approaching Jericho. The crowds are increasing all the time as tributary streams join themselves to the main body which is making its way to the Passover at Jerusalem. There should therefore be a background of crowd noise with occasional laughter and children's shouts.*)

MATTHEW (*enthusiastically*). Doesn't it do your heart good, Judas, to be walking in the Master's own party like this? There must be thousands of people taking this road to Jerusalem, and the dust is enough to choke you. But we're the chosen Twelve, and it feels good to me going up to the Passover like this.

JUDAS (*firmly*). This trudging in the dust isn't good enough for the Master, Matthew. He ought to be mounted, in splendor! And as for us?—Well, I think we ought to be outriders for the King. I believe he's going to his greatest triumph. There ought to be cheers and music and trumpets!

MATTHEW (*placatingly*). Well, perhaps there will be

77

when we get a bit nearer the city. But (*ruefully*) for the moment it seems to me our job is to be a sort of bodyguard to keep the crowds at a reasonable distance.

JUDAS (*contemptuously*). The crowds! They get excited enough when they recognize him, but d'you suppose they have the slightest idea of who it is that they're cheering?

MATTHEW. No, but then, why should they? All they know is that he's been a friend to them. He's healed their diseases, and given them hope and faith.

PETER. Matthew!

MATTHEW. Well, what is it, Peter?

PETER. The Master says we're going to stop here in this olive grove just off the road and let some of the crowds go by.

JUDAS. Right. We shan't be sorry for a bit of shade.

(*A short pause and footsteps, and fade in voices of other disciples.*)

PETER. Master, these Pharisees with all their rules and regulations think they're the only ones who are right. You can tell, from the way they talk, they look down on all the rest of us. As for tax collectors, they're reckoned the lowest of the low. Didn't you find that, Matthew?

MATTHEW. I certainly did, Peter! Master, how does the Father look upon all these people—the so-called saints and the ordinary sinners?

JESUS. The Father sees the hearts of men. That is why the judgments of men are often wrong. Do you remember the scripture, "Man looketh upon the outward appearance but God looketh upon the heart"? Yes, God sees the hearts of men, and that is why there are many things which men consider perfectly splendid, but which are utterly detestable in the eyes of the Father. Let me tell you all a story.

One day two men went up to the Temple to pray, one was a Pharisee, and the other was a tax collector. The Pharisee stood and prayed to himself like this: "God, I thank thee that I am not like other men, greedy, dishonest, impure, or even like that tax collector over there. I fast twice every week; I give away a tenth part of all my income."

But the tax collector stood in a distant corner, scarcely daring to look up to Heaven, and with a gesture of despair, said, "God have mercy on a sinner like me." I tell you truly that *he* was the man who went home accepted in God's sight rather than the other one. For everyone who sets himself up as somebody will become a nobody, and the man who makes himself a nobody will become somebody!

Then Jesus entered and passed through Jericho, and behold, there was a man called Zacchaeus, which was the chief among the tax collectors, and he was rich. And he sought to see Jesus who he was; and could not because of the crowd since he was small in stature, and he ran before and climbed up into a sycamore tree to see Jesus; for he was to pass that way.

(*Murmur of crowd. Bystanders' voices in the following scene should be rural in accent.*)

1ST BYSTANDER (*a bit ironically*). Here he comes now with his precious Twelve. Now you'll all be able to see what he's like!

2ND BYSTANDER (*heatedly*). Yes, and you won't be disappointed. I've seen him before. I've seen him heal
the sick and cast out devils.

1ST BYSTANDER. All right, all right. No offense meant, but
I've never known anything like this. Everyone wants
to see him. Why, even the trees are full of boys who
are determined to see him. Look like a lot of crows!

3RD BYSTANDER (*in a hoarse but penetrating whisper*).
Yes, don't look now, but there's one particular carrion
crow perched right over our heads.

1ST BYSTANDER. What, that rascal, Zacchaeus? Has he
climbed up there?

3RD BYSTANDER. Shsh! Here comes Jesus of Nazareth.
Peace be to you, Master!

JESUS. And peace to you, also. (*Pause.*) Zacchaeus, hurry
up and come down from your perch. I am going to be
your guest today!

ZACCHAEUS (*Taken aback*). *My* guest? (*Confused.*) Of
course, of course, delighted, honored—be down as
quick as I can!

(*Noise of scrabbling, breaking of small branches, etc.*)

1ST BYSTANDER. So that's where the little miser was!

2ND BYSTANDER. I don't wonder he hid himself.

JUDAS. Master, this is the biggest swindler of the lot—
Surely you're not going to stay with him? Why, people
don't even speak to him unless they have to! He's a
real sinner, that one.

JESUS. Judas, do you not remember the story I told you
as we came along the road?

ZACCHAEUS (*rather breathless*). Sir, sir, you do me great
honor! I promise I will give half my property to the
poor. (*An ironical cheer.*) Yes, and what is more, if I

have swindled anybody out of anything, I swear I will pay them back four times as much. (*Another small cheer.*)

1ST BYSTANDER (*derisively*). Now that's what I call a real miracle!

JESUS. Zacchaeus, this is the day of salvation for you and your household. Remember, all of you, that whatever he has done, Zacchaeus is as truly one of God's people as any one of you. I am entering the house of a man whom you regard as an outsider, and if in your hearts you are criticizing me, remember what I have said before: The Son of Man has not come to call the righteous together, but to seek, and to save, the lost.

CHRIST ENTERS JERUSALEM

And it came to pass, when Jesus was come nigh to Beth-
phage and Bethany, at the mount called the Mount of
Olives, he sent two of his disciples, saying, Go ye into the
village over against you. There, as ye enter ye shall find
a colt tied, whereon never man yet sat: loose him, and
bring him hither. And if any man ask you, Why do ye loose
him? thus shall ye say unto him, Because the Lord hath
need of him.

(Stamping of hoofs.)

JAMES. Whoa, there, you young rascal! Here, Master.
Here's the colt. Keep still, old fellow. I don't think he
liked being dragged out of his stall so early in the
morning!

JOHN. Yes, it was just as well we fetched him before the
crowds got on the move again. One minute he was
kicking and pulling all over the place, and then he'd
dig his hoofs into the dust and roll his eyes at us.

JAMES. *And,* they told us at the village that no one has
ever ridden on him yet. Are you sure he's the right
one, Master?

JESUS (*gently*). Yes, you're the right one, aren't you, young fellow? (*Noise of patting of colt's neck, and satisfied whinnying.*) He'll be all right now. James, just hold him gently until I come back. I shall not be long.

JAMES. Yes Master. Come on, young fellow: that's right. Come on now.

PETER (*in some surprise*). Look, John, he's perfectly still and quiet! I've seen that happen to *people* often enough. But as for animals . . .

JOHN. Simple, Peter. He was just plain scared, and the Master's made him feel happy. (*Coaxingly to the colt*) There, he made you feel that he loved you—wasn't that it, old boy? Here, steady on, there's no need to eat my cloak! You'll have a good feed in Jerusalem when all this is over.

(*Pause.*)

PETER. How beautiful the Holy City looks in the early morning light! I feel this is going to be a wonderful day for all of us. I feel joy and triumph in the air. What d'you think, Judas?

JUDAS (*harshly*). It ought to be a triumph, but it's certainly not the way I would have planned it. If he's the Master, he ought to go riding in, properly mounted like a conqueror, instead of trotting along on this poor beast.

PETER. Well, it's his own choice, Judas.

JUDAS. I know, I know. Well, at least he needn't ride bareback. Here's my cloak for a start.

PETER. And here's mine. And let's have yours too, Andrew.

(*Offers of cloaks from disciples.*)

JOHN. Any minute now the people will be round us as they were yesterday.

PETER. And the crowds'll get thicker as we get near the city, that's certain.

JAMES. Yes, they told us in the village early this morning that people are planning some sort of reception.

PETER (*cheerfully*). Well, now we're all set. But where's the Master?

JAMES. Quiet, Peter! Quiet all of you. (*Quietly*) He's over there, just looking and looking at the city.

PETER (*dropping his voice*). Yes, I've seen that set look on his face before, and I don't like it.

JUDAS (*tensely, in lowered tones*). But there's no need for it, no need at all. If only he'd listen to me.

PETER (*in a hoarse whisper*). Listen to you, Judas! Once his mind's made up, he'll listen to no man—only to the Father.

(*Pause.*)

JOHN. Be quiet both of you, can't you see how strained he looks.

JESUS (*deeply moved*). O Jerusalem, Jerusalem, how many prophets of God have you stoned to death! Alas, how blind you have been! (*Pause.*) How I have longed over you! How gladly would I have gathered your children around me, but you would never let me. (*Pause.*) If only you could see, now at the very last, what would bring you true peace. But you cannot, you will not, see—even when God sends His own Son to visit you. O Jerusalem, Jerusalem, the time will surely come when your enemies will utterly destroy you, because you are so proud, so blind. O Jerusalem, Jerusalem!

(*Pause.*)

And when Jesus was come near to the city even now at the descent of the mount of Olives, the whole multitude of the disciples began to rejoice and praise God with a loud voice for all the mighty works that they had seen.

(*Fade in excited voices of crowd.*)

LITTLE BOY'S VOICE (*excitedly*). Is he coming, is he coming? Shall I be able to see him? Who is he, father?

FATHER (*lifts him up, with a grunt*). There—there you are, safe on my shoulder, and you'll see better than the tallest man in the crowd. They say it's the man Jesus. . . .

LITTLE BOY. What, the man who heals people? Some of the boys at school have seen him, *and* heard him talk. They say he's wonderful!

FATHER. Yes, my son, some people think he's the Messiah.

LITTLE BOY (*awed*). *The Messiah!*

A VOICE (*ringing out above noise of crowd*). God bless the One who comes in the name of the Lord!

ANOTHER VOICE. Aye, God bless him!

LITTLE BOY. I can see him, I can see him now! People have put down their coats in the road—it's like a carpet for a king! And lots of them are waving palm branches.

VOICES. Hosanna, Hosanna, Hosanna in the highest!

OTHER VOICES. God bless the Messiah, the Savior, the King!

MORE VOICES. Praise the Lord! God bless His Chosen, His Anointed!

A VOICE (*shouting above the din*). Listen, all of you, is not this the prophecy of Zechariah come true, when

he said, "Fear not, daughter of Sion, behold thy King
cometh sitting on an ass's colt?"

VOICES.   Hosanna, Hosanna!

(*And the crowd noises resume as before, and this short
conversation must take place against those noises.*)

A PHARISEE (*sternly*).   Can you hear me, Jesus of Nazareth, above the shouts of this mob of yours? We
Pharisees do all we can to make this Feast of the
Passover a solemn and a spiritual thing. Can you not
stop this unseemly noise among your followers?

JESUS.   No, today I cannot stop them. Indeed I tell you
that if they were silenced the very stones by the road-
side would be shouting their praise!

(*The cheering resumes, and then fades.*)

And when Jesus was come into Jerusalem, all the city
was moved, saying. Who is this? And the multitude said,
This is Jesus, the prophet of Nazareth of Galilee.

⚛ 16 ⚛

THE CLEANSING OF THE TEMPLE

*(Scene: The Courtyard of the Temple. There should be the
noise of sheep and oxen; the cooing of doves; the chink of
money and the murmur of the crowds. Also something like
the occasional clanking of a bucket to suggest the carrying
of secular objects through the courtyard.*

The TWO PHARISEES *are overlooking the courtyard from
above, the older is a Pharisee of the old school, and the
other is very young.)*

OLDER PHARISEE *(disdainfully).* Looking down from here
we can see it all, and this is a part of the Feast which
I confess I dislike intensely. All this noise, all this
haggling, not to speak of the smell! I tell you, when I
was a young Pharisee like you, we should never have
allowed even the outer courts of the Temple to be used
like this.

YOUNG PHARISEE *(respectfully, but firmly).* I see your
point of view, sir. Not one of us likes this sort of thing,
but what can we do? The city has grown since your
younger days, and every year more and more of our
people come to the Feast. After all, they've got to

87

make their sacrifices, and where else could they decently buy them?

OLDER PHARISEE (*sharply*). Decently you say? It sounds more like a cattle market to me, and I wouldn't be surprised if there's a good deal of cheating at those exchange tables.

YOUNG PHARISEE. Oh, come sir, you don't know that! These people have come from all kinds of outlandish parts. You wouldn't have Temple taxes paid in greasy Gentile money, surely?

OLDER PHARISEE. No, of course not, and I also know, young man, that a money-changer is allowed to change a small percentage for his trouble. But look at that woman there—"farmer's wife" written all over her. Good and pious, I have no doubt, but how can she know whether she's being cheated or not? And she must be astonished to find the price of a pair of doves or a young lamb is about a dozen times what it would be on her farm.

YOUNG PHARISEE. Well, of course, sir, if that's true it's a pity, but I must admit I hear very few grumbles. People have grown used to it. I don't suppose things are worse here than in any other market place.

OLDER PHARISEE (*passionately*). But this is *not a* market place! This is the Court of Gentiles, part of the House of God. Everything here should be holy unto the Lord. But it's always the same with the common people— give them an inch and they'll take a yard. We give them this part of the courtyard for this necessary business—and what do they do? Instead of conducting their business reverently and quietly they shout, laugh, bawl and argue.

YOUNG PHARISEE (*with a tolerant half laugh*).   But surely, sir, that's human nature everywhere?

OLDER PHARISEE (*angrily*).   But not human nature in the House of God! Why, half of them use this courtyard as a short cut. I've seen them, while we've been talking, carrying their tools, their waterpots, their bundles of carpet right through the crowd, and even singing or whistling as they go. They've long ago forgotten it's the House of God. Mark my words, I'll say something at our next meeting!

YOUNG PHARISEE.   But, sir, we must move with the times. The power of the people is very great. We cannot afford . . .

OLDER PHARISEE (*scornfully*).   Cannot afford! When I was your age, young man, people did what they were told. We taught them to worship God. Yes, we spoke in the name of the Lord, and they obeyed.

YOUNG PHARISEE (*placatingly*).   Yes, I'm sure they did, sir. (*With sudden interest.*) But what's that going on down below?

(*All the voices stop, though naturally a few animal noises persist.*)

OLDER PHARISEE.   What's happened. Why's everyone stopped talking?

YOUNG PHARISEE.   It's that young fellow from Nazareth, sir. He's a sort of hero with the people. (*With relish.*) Now let's see how Jesus deals with *this* situation.

JESUS.   Take all these things away. Is not this the house of prayer? My Father's House? Out! Out! Away with all these sheep and oxen. Out with you and your doves, and out with you, you rogues who would dare to cheat in my Father's House!

(There is confused noise here of hoofs, cattle bellowing, cries of "Shame!" "He's right, you know!" "I've been cheated here for years!"—and of course crashes as money-changers' tables are overturned.)

JESUS. Out, I say. Away with you. Begone, begone. I command you, cleanse this house of evil. Do not the Scriptures say that here in the Temple all nations may come to worship God? My Father's House is a place of prayer for all nations and you have turned this Court of the Gentiles into a market.

VOICE. Well done, Master! That should have been done years ago!

WOMAN'S VOICE. Hear, hear! Every year I come here to worship, but before I can pray I have to get through this thieving mob. But the people are behind you, Master, and there'll be many glad for what you've done this day.

JESUS. Thank you, my daughter. It is written, My father's House shall be a house of prayer. A house of prayer for all nations. . . . And what have they done? They have made it a den of thieves.

(Fade out to complete silence. A short pause.)

YOUNG PHARISEE *(rather bitterly)*. Well, sir, all that you complained of has been cleared out. Are you satisfied now?

OLDER PHARISEE. No, not satisfied. We're the ones who should have cleared up this evil, not this young man from—where is it—Nazareth?

YOUNG PHARISEE. I agree, sir. *(Slyly)* The people are eating out of that young man's hand. It could be dangerous for all of us.

OLDER PHARISEE (*grimly*). Yes. And it could also be dangerous for Jesus of Nazareth.

And the chief priests and the scribes heard of this, and sought how they might destroy Jesus: for they feared him, because all the people were astonished at his teaching. And when even was come, he went out of the city.

∾ 17 ∾

THE PARABLE OF THE
LAST JUDGMENT

(*Scene: One of the courts of the Temple.* JESUS *is surrounded by a crowd.*)

And Jesus taught daily in the Temple, but the chief priests and the scribes and the elders of the people sought to destroy him.

(*A subdued but expectant murmur from a large crowd.*)

A PEASANT VOICE (*gratefully*).   Master, we've had a wonderful week listening to your teaching.

VARIOUS VOICES.
Aye, that we have.
Hear, hear!
This is stuff we can understand.
Some of it, anyway.
Makes more sense than what the Scribes and Pharisees preach at us.

PEASANT VOICE.   But what happens in the end, Master?

VOICE.   Yes, is there a judgment after death?

ANOTHER VOICE.   Tell us about that, sir!

JESUS.   Yes, I will answer you. In the end, the Son of Man will come in glory and take his seat upon his throne. All nations will be assembled before him and he will separate them as a shepherd divides his flock, the sheep on his right hand and the goats on his left. He will turn to those on his right and say to them, "Come, all of you whom my Father loves, and possess the kingdom which has been yours from the beginning of the world."

VOICE (*complacently*).   Ah, that'll be us Jews, won't it?

ANOTHER VOICE.   Shsh! Be quiet, let the Master finish.

JESUS (*continuing as though not interrupted*).   And the Son of Man will say to them, "I was hungry and you gave me food. I was thirsty and you gave me drink. I was a stranger and you invited me into your homes. I was in rags and you gave me clothes. I was ill and you visited me. Yes, and even when I was in prison you came to see me." Then the good men will say, "But when did we ever see *you* hungry or thirsty. When did we see you ill or in any kind of trouble or need and look after *you?*" Then the King, who is the Son of Man, shall tell them, "Whenever and wherever you did these things for the least important of my brother men you did them—(*Pause*)—for me."

JUDAS (*scandalized*).   But, Master, what are you saying? This means there will be men in your kingdom who haven't even followed you! Why, it opens the door to all kinds of people!

VOICE.   Be quiet, you! The Master knows what he is saying.

JESUS (*continues as though without interruption*).   Then the Son of Man will turn to those on his left and he will send them away from God's presence to the place of destruction. He will say to them, "I was hungry and

you gave me no food; I was thirsty and you gave me
nothing to drink; I was in rags and you gave me no
clothes; I was ill and in prison and you never came to
see me." But they will say to him, "But, Lord, whenever did we see *you* hungry or thirsty, lonely, ill or in
prison and fail to look after *you?*" And the Son of Man
will answer them, "Whenever and wherever you failed
to serve the least important of my brothers you failed
to serve me."

(*Pause.*)

VOICE. Master, we never heard teaching like that before!
ANOTHER VOICE. It rings true to me, but it needs some
thinking about.
1ST VOICE. Aye, that it does.

(*Fade voices and murmurs.*)
(*Scene: High Priest's Palace.*)

Then assembled together the chief priests, and the
scribes, and the elders of the people, unto the palace of the
high priest, who was called Caiaphas. And they consulted
how they might take Jesus secretly, and kill him. But they
said, Not on the feast day, lest there be an uproar among
the people.

HIGH PRIEST. Gentlemen, at least we're all agreed that
this man Jesus is a danger to us all—not to us personally, of course, but to the whole sacred system of the
Law. This very week he took it upon himself to clear
the Temple courts of all that offended him. He did
right. (*A murmur of discontent.*) Ah, yes, some of you
may feel he was right—that there were abuses. But

who is this Jesus who thinks that he has some divine
right to come into God's holy Temple and cleanse it?
His fantastic and blasphemous claims destroy our
authority, our God-given authority, I would remind
you! (*With sudden venom*) He must be got out of
the way! (*Murmur of approval.*) But always we come
back to the same question—HOW are we to arrest
him? It would be impossible here in Jerusalem. Somehow we must get the man on his own.

(*Murmurs of: "Indeed yes." "The crowds are all on his
side." "We can't risk a riot."*)

CHIEF PRIEST.   Gentlemen, I think I may have found the
answer to our problem.

(*Pause.*)

HIGH PRIEST.   Then speak, man, the matter is urgent.

CHIEF PRIEST.   Well, it so happens that late last night I met
one of Jesus' followers, a bitter and disillusioned man.
I believe he knows where this man Jesus could be
found outside the city. His name is Judas Iscariot.

HIGH PRIEST.   Well, get hold of the man and bring him to
us! Time is running short.

CHIEF PRIEST.   I have already taken the liberty of bringing
him here. He's waiting outside. Officer!

OFFICER.   Sir?

CHIEF PRIEST.   Bring in the man.

OFFICER.   Yes, sir.

HIGH PRIEST.   Gentlemen, this may be our one chance before the Passover. You will be kind enough to let me
deal with him.

CHIEF PRIEST.   Here is your man, sir!

HIGH PRIEST.   Ah, Judas Iscariot! You are a follower of this
Jesus of Nazareth?

JUDAS. I was, for many months. I thought him to be the Messiah. Indeed, I was prepared . . .

HIGH PRIEST (*coldly*). We're not interested in your thoughts. All we want to know from you is this: Is there some quiet place away from the crowds where you know the man Jesus will be?

JUDAS. There is such a place. He goes there after dark.

HIGH PRIEST. And can you lead us there?

JUDAS. I can.

HIGH PRIEST. Then will you give us this piece of information? It need not be on your conscience. We, the leaders of the Jewish people, know what is best for our nation.

JUDAS (*bitterly*). Conscience! I have no conscience about this man. It is *I* who have been betrayed and disillusioned. I . . .

HIGH PRIEST. May I remind you again that we are not interested in your thoughts or feelings. All we want from you is information leading to the arrest of the man.

JUDAS (*truculently*). And what do I get for this precious information.

HIGH PRIEST (*with contempt*). Well, there will be—a fee, of course. Shall we say thirty pieces of silver?

JUDAS (*laughing bitterly*). Thirty pieces of silver to pay for the king . . . (*recovering himself*) . . . but you're not interested in my feelings. I accept your offer. After dark I will take you myself to where I know he will be.

HIGH PRIEST. Thank you, Judas Iscariot. Here is the silver.

~ 18 ~

THE LAST SUPPER

(Scene: The Upper Room where JESUS *has arranged to eat the Passover with his disciples.*

We may imagine that the scene opens when the Passover meal, itself a rather silent affair, is almost over.)

And on the first day of Unleavened Bread, when they sacrificed the passover lamb, his disciples said to him, "Where will you have us go and prepare for you to eat the passover?"

And he sent two of his disciples, and said to them, "Go into the city, and a man carrying a jar of water will meet you; follow him, and wherever he enters, say to the householder, 'The Master says, "Where is my guest room, where I am to eat the passover with my disciples?"' And he will show you a large upper room furnished and ready; there prepare for us." And the disciples set out and went to the city, and found it as he had told them; and they prepared the passover.

And when it was evening, Jesus came with the twelve.

JESUS. My friends, you have been with me from the begin-

ning. You do not know how I have longed to eat this
Passover with you all—before I suffer.

PETER (*impulsively*).   Master, you do not know how sad
you make us feel when you talk like that. You have
enemies, but you also have many friends.

JUDAS (*almost ferociously*).   And if you would have allowed it, your friends would have put you in power
long before this!

JAMES (*horrified*).   Judas!

JUDAS (*grimly*).   I know what I'm talking about.

JESUS.   My children, as I have told you before, the Son of
Man must take the path that is appointed for him. But
it will be one of his closest friends who will betray him.
(*Half to himself*) Alas, for that man—better for him if
he had never been born!

JOHN.   But surely, Master, none of us who love you would
ever betray you?

JESUS (*with sad certainty*).   The one who betrays me will
be one of my chosen Twelve.

(*Voices of consternation and horror.*)

JAMES.   Surely, Master, you don't think it's me?

MATTHEW.   Or me, Master?

PETER.   You know that none of us would ever say a word
against you.

JESUS.   Yet I tell you truly that it will be one of you Twelve
who are sharing this meal with me.

(*Fresh murmurs of:* "*Who can he mean?*" "*Which of us
would do such a thing?*" "*Doesn't he trust us?*")

JUDAS (*in a hoarse whisper*).   Master, d'you think *I* would
betray you?

JESUS (*quietly*).   Judas, you know the answer to that

question. (*The strain showing in his voice*) Whatever you do, do it quickly. (*More loudly*) Now listen to me, my Twelve. We have eaten this Passover together. See, I take this loaf and break it. (*He prays.*) Praised be Thou, O Lord our God, King of the world, who causest bread to come forth from the earth. (*Short pause.*) Now take it, and share it among yourselves. Take it, Peter. (*Very deliberately*) It is my body, which is given for you. You are to eat it in remembrance of me.

And now, see, I take the cup of wine. (*He prays.*) Praised be Thou, O Lord, King of the universe, thou who feedest the whole world with goodness, grace and mercy. Drink from it. Take it, John. It is my blood, shed for you and for many, for the forgiveness of sins.

And supper being ended, the devil having now put into the heart of Judas Iscariot to betray him; Jesus, knowing that he was come from God and went to God; he riseth from supper and laid aside his garments; and took a towel and girded himself. After that he poureth water into a basin and began to wash the disciples' feet.

(*In order to avoid cataloguing the whole Twelve, there could be at this point a murmuring of voices, the noise of water, before bringing up the voice of* JESUS.)

JESUS (*gently*). Now James and John, I have washed your feet just as I have washed the others.
JAMES AND JOHN (*meekly together*).   Yes, Master.
JESUS.   And now I must do the same for you, Matthew.
MATTHEW (*nervously*).   Only because you say so, Master.
JESUS.   And for you too, Judas, I do the work of a servant.
JUDAS (*harshly, with a hint of contempt*).   So I see.

JESUS (*gently*). And lastly, Peter, I come to you. Take off your sandals, and I will wash your feet.

PETER (*horrified*). Never. You are our Master, our Lord! I cannot bear to see you kneeling there doing such things for us.

JESUS (*seriously, but not unkindly*). Peter, unless you allow me to do this thing, you cannot go on with me.

PETER. Then wash me, Master! Not only my feet, but my whole body.

JESUS (*gently and firmly*). That is not necessary, Peter. The man whose body has been washed only needs to wash the dust off his feet. You whom I have chosen are clean men (*half to himself*), though alas, not all of you.

VOICES. Oh, Master!

JESUS. My children, I wonder if you know what I have just done for you. You call me "Master" and "Lord," and that is quite right, for I am both your Master and your Lord. But I have given you an example to follow. For if I your Lord and Master have washed your feet, you must be ready and willing to do such things for one another. All over the world men use power over others, but it must not be so among you. Indeed, if any of you wants to rule he must be willing to be the servant of you all. For I, the Son of Man, am among you, not to be served, but to serve.

PETER (*strongly moved*). Master, there is no one like you! I would go anywhere with you, even to prison. Yes, I would even die with you!

JESUS (*sadly*). Peter, I tell you that this very night before the cock crows you will disown me three times.

PETER (*vehemently*). Never, Lord, even if I had to die with you, I would never disown you!

JAMES (*warmly*).   And neither would any of us!

MATTHEW (*defiantly*).   We will stay by you, Master, whatever happens.

JOHN.   Master, can you not see that we love you? We will never desert you.

JESUS (*very gently, but sadly*).   My little children, the time is very near now that you will be scattered to your own homes and will leave me alone. And yet I am not alone because the Father is with me. You must not be anxious, you must not be dismayed. Believe in the Father, and believe in me.

And when they had sung a hymn they went out to the Mount of Olives.

∾ 19 ∾

THE ARREST IN THE GARDEN

(Scene: The Garden of Gethsemane.)

JAMES.   How beautiful and quiet it is here in the garden,
John, here where we've so often been with the Master!

JOHN.   Yes, but beautiful things often make me feel sad.
We both know it's not only that; it's the way the
Master's been talking, as though disaster were just
round the corner.

JAMES.   And the way he's been behaving. I felt the tears
come to my eyes when he insisted on washing our feet
like that.

JOHN.   Yes, I felt the same. Hello, here's Peter. What does
he want?

PETER.   Have you two seen Judas? I thought we were *all*
to meet here?

JAMES.   No, we haven't seen him, since the supper, that is.

JOHN.   But I do seem to remember the Master sending
him out on some errand or other, and telling him to be
quick about it.

PETER.   Oh, Master, you startled me!

JESUS.   Where else should I be on this night, except here
with my friends? James and John, and you too, Peter,

come with me a little further into the garden. The rest
of you sit down here for a while.

DISCIPLES. Yes, Master.

JESUS. And, as you love me, pray for me. Peter, James,
John, you three have been alone with me before. This
is my hour of deepest sorrow. Stay here, pray, and
keep watch with me. I shall not go far away.

PETER. That we will, Master.

JAMES. Yes, Master.

JOHN. We will pray and keep watch.

(*A short pause.*)

JESUS. O, my Father, if it is possible, let me not have to
face this. Everything is possible to you—but it is your
will and not mine that must be done. O, my Father,
my Father . . .

(*Fade out voice of* JESUS.)

Then he cometh unto the disciples and findeth them
asleep.

JESUS. Oh, Peter, couldn't you keep watch with me for a
single hour? You must keep awake and you must pray.
How else can you avoid falling into the power of
temptation? Your spirit is willing enough but human
nature is, alas, weak.

(*Short pause.*)

O, my Father, my Father, I do not seek to do my will
but yours. Give me strength, to suffer what I must
suffer, to bear what I must bear, that the Son may be
glorified in the Father. But *if* it be possible let this cup
pass from me—but no, your will be done, your will be
done . . .

(*Fade out voice of* JESUS.)

And Jesus came and found them asleep again; for their eyes were heavy. And he left them, and went away again, and prayed the third time, saying the same words. Then cometh Jesus to his disciples.

(*Note*—JESUS *is now utterly resolute, and there is steel in his voice as he speaks to the disciples. He speaks quite loudly for the words are ironical.*)

JESUS. Sleep on now, the watch is over! The fight is won, now you can rest!

PETER (*sadly*). Oh, Master, we never meant to sleep.

JAMES. We did try, but we just couldn't keep our eyes open.

JESUS (*brusquely*). James, that's enough! (*Noise of approaching crowd.*) Wake up, all of you, and open your eyes. Now is the time for the Son of Man to be betrayed, yes, betrayed into the hands of evil men.

(*While he is still speaking the noise of a crowd grows rapidly, with possibly shouts of "Are you sure this is the place?" "Where is the man?" "Let's get at him!"*)

JUDAS. Remember, the one I kiss—that is the man. (*Murmured response.*)

JESUS (*deliberately*). Judas, my friend, what made you come here?

JUDAS (*with mock heartiness*). Master, how *good* to see you!

JESUS. Judas, do you betray the Son of Man with a kiss?

VOICES. We've got him! Hold him fast!

JESUS. So you've all come out to catch me with your swords and staves. Day after day I sat there in the

Temple and not one of you dared to lay a finger on me. Do you think I have no power against you even now? I have only to ask my Father and the hosts of Heaven would be at my side to defend me! But that is not how it must be. The scriptures must be fulfilled and you are fulfilling them. Here in the dark you will do the work of darkness.

(*A moment's pause—and the murderous roar of the crowd rises.*)

Then all the disciples forsook him and fled. And they led Jesus away to the High Priest, where all the scribes and priests and elders were assembled. And Peter followed him afar off, even into the palace of the High Priest; and he sat with the servants and warmed himself at the fire.

1ST SERVANT. B-r-r-r-r, it's cold! (*Rubs his hands together.*) Well, we've caught him, and very little trouble, I must say.

2ND SERVANT. Well, it'll be hot enough inside there for this Jesus. I must say, in a way I admire him. Hey, girl, bring us some wine!

MAIDSERVANT (*pertly*). Certainly, sir.

1ST SERVANT. Admire him? Well, yes, I suppose you might, but the man is a fool. Who but a fool would pit himself against all our crowd—chief priests, scribes, pharisees, elders, all of them? Oh, thanks, girl.

MAIDSERVANT. You're welcome! And here's yours, sir.

2ND SERVANT. Thanks. Well, I can't say I've enjoyed this night's work. Here's to the downfall of Rome.

1ST SERVANT. Downfall of Rome!

MAIDSERVANT (*to Peter*). Hello, stranger, keeping warm by our fire?

PETER.   Yes, lass.

MAIDSERVANT.   Come to the wicked city and lost your fortune, eh? Ow! How stupid of me! (*Seriously*) You must be a friend of our hero upstairs—is that it?

PETER (*desperately*).   Let me get out of here, girl. I don't know what you're talking about. I've never heard of your hero!

MAIDSERVANT (*cheekily*).   Oo, temper! (*Pause.*) Why don't you go up the stairs and get a breath of fresh air?

PETER.   That's just where I am going!

2ND GIRL.   That's one of them, you know, one of those followers of Jesus. Looks like the end of the world, doesn't he?

PETER (*as from a slight distance*).   Leave me alone, all of you. I never knew him, and I don't know what you're talking about. I need fresh air!

2ND GIRL.   Go on, then, up the steps, and first on your right.

(*Noise of* PETER'S *footsteps up stone stairs, muttering to himself as he goes.*)

PETER (*in utter misery*).   Oh, God, oh, God, this is the end. You know I hoped, I trusted, I even tried to fight a bit. And now, oh, God, they've got him. . . .

A VOICE (*possibly slightly in his cups*).   Hello. What are you looking so miserable about?

PETER (*impatiently*).   Let me go!

VOICE.   Oh, come on, don't be so unfriendly. I love that Galilean voice of yours. Reminds me of my childhood. But (*in sudden shocked sobriety*) Galilean, are you? Friend of the poor fellow up above, eh?

PETER (*with furious vehemence*).   Curse you! How dare you speak of Galilee? I swear to you I've never even heard of the man up above! Now get out of my way!

(*The cock crows.*)

And Peter remembered the word of Jesus which said unto him, Before the cock crow, thou shalt deny me thrice. And he went out, and wept bitterly.

∞ 20 ∞

THE TRIAL BEFORE PILATE

(*Scene: Pilate's Court.*)

And straightway in the early morning the chief priests held a consultation with the elders and scribes and the whole council, and they bound Jesus, and led him away, and delivered him to Pontius Pilate.

PILATE. Centurion!

CENTURION. Sir.

PILATE (*irritably*). What's all that noise outside? Send someone to quieten them down.

CENTURION. Yes, sir.

PILATE. Clerk of the Court, be seated. Centurion!

CENTURION. Sir.

PILATE. Bring the Jewish leaders in, but keep that mob out of here. If I wish to speak to them I shall use the balcony.

CENTURION. Understood, sir.

PILATE. Clerk of the Court!

CLERK OF COURT. Yes, sir.

PILATE. Make careful note of these proceedings.

(*While he is speaking there is the noise of door flung open, and the noise of footsteps. The murmur of the mob rises as the door opens and is subdued as it is shut. There is a moment's pause.*)

CENTURION (*announcing*).   The Jewish leaders, sir.

PILATE (*formally*).   Greetings to you, my Lord Caiaphas, and to the rest of you gentlemen. Pray be seated.

CAIAPHAS.   We prefer to stand. The matter is of the utmost urgency.

PILATE.   What is this "utmost urgency"? I do not care for the very early morning.

CAIAPHAS.   There is a man here in Jerusalem, your Excellency, called Jesus of Nazareth, who has secured an enormous following among the people. They listen in their thousands to him instead of to us, God's appointed leaders of the Jewish people.

PILATE.   But that is a purely Jewish matter. I am not prepared to try a man because he has hurt your pride!

CAIAPHAS.   Your Excellency, this is not a question of our pride. I tell you that this Jesus has enormous power among the people. (*Deliberately*) He may well prove a danger to the authority of Rome.

PILATE.   A danger to the authority of Rome? I have had reports about this man for some months now, and some of my observers were favorably impressed with him.

CAIAPHAS.   Then perhaps your observers did not hear his claim to be a king—or possibly they did not care to report that to you.

PILATE (*astonished*).   A king?

CAIAPHAS.   Yes, a king—a king who claims to be superior not only to us, but to Caesar himself.

PILATE (*sharply*).   Clerk, write down that charge! Centurion, bring the prisoner in.

CENTURION.   Yes, sir.

(*Sounds of footsteps of* CENTURION *going off to fetch* JESUS, *and again later when the two return.*)

PILATE.   This is a very serious matter, my Lord Caiaphas. I take it you have witnesses to prove your accusation.

CAIAPHAS.   Indeed I have. All of us here have heard much about him and his kingdom.

1ST PRIEST.   Indeed we have!

CENTURION.   The prisoner, sir. The man from Nazareth.

PILATE.   Jesus of Nazareth, I'll come straight to the point. *Are* you the king of the Jews?

JESUS.   What you have said is true.

2ND PRIEST.   That's a lie! He's a carpenter!

CAIAPHAS.   He cannot deny that he has been teaching all our people that he is the king of some strange kingdom.

1ST PRIEST.   Yes, and more than once I've heard him, with my own ears, claim to forgive sins.

2ND PRIEST.   It's utter blasphemy!

PILATE.   A moment, gentlemen. Jesus, have you anything to say in reply to these charges which they make against you?

(*Pause.*)

PILATE.   What, nothing? (*Further pause.*) Very well. Gentlemen, these matters really concern your own religion. If the prisoner has grown above himself I will have him beaten and released later. What do you say to that?

2ND PRIEST.   He deserves to die!

PILATE (*icily*).   Indeed? I find nothing criminal about him.

CAIAPHAS.   Your Excellency, perhaps my colleague's enthusiasm for our religion has obscured the real danger. Here is a man, undoubtedly attempting to make himself a king. That he cannot deny. I do not bring this charge irresponsibly.

PILATE.   Then I will examine the prisoner closely. Centurion, bring the man Jesus to me in my private room.

CENTURION.   Yes, sir!

(Sound of footsteps.)

CAIAPHAS (*speaking quickly, in great excitement*).   Now listen to me, all of you! We must work, and work fast.

1ST PRIEST.   But what do you want us to do?

CAIAPHAS.   Do? I want every one of you to get to work on the crowd. Tell them it is essential that every man shows himself loyal to Caesar. Wait a moment, if Pilate tries to release Jesus through the old custom at festival time, get them shouting for Barabbas instead. For Barabbas, you understand? Barabbas!

(Fade out voice.)

PILATE.   Now Jesus, who *are* you? Where do you come from? Are you really a king?

JESUS.   I am indeed a king. The time will come when all men shall know that I am king, not of the Jews only, but of the whole world.

PILATE.   So you're a king, are you? Well, then, why don't your followers fight for you?

JESUS.   My kingdom is not that kind of kingdom. It is not founded in this world at all. But everyone who recognizes the truth knows that my claim is true.

PILATE.   Truth! How is a man in my position to know

what is truth? But (*half to himself*) I'll save you if I can, despite your Jewish leaders. (*He calls.*) Centurion, keep guard here while I have a further word with Master Caiaphas.

CENTURION.　Yes, sir.

(*The door closes and there are footsteps heard as* PONTIUS PILATE *advances toward* CAIAPHAS.)

PILATE.　Well now, Caiaphas, you'll be glad to know I find nothing criminal about your fellow countryman at all.

CAIAPHAS.　I take it then, your Excellency, you see no danger.

PILATE (*cheerfully*).　None at all!

CAIAPHAS (*playing his last card*).　Then I must tell you that this very day we heard him claim to be the Son of God. That is blasphemy, and by our law he deserves death. I warn you, you take a grave risk if you arouse the wrath of our people.

PILATE.　Well, we'll see about that. (*To* CENTURION) Unbar the balcony—I wish to address the crowd!

(*Noise of unbolting of protective iron screen and of its being drawn back. There is a tumultuous roar as* PONTIUS PILATE *appears on balcony.*)

VOICE (*harshly, above roar of crowd*).　According to our law, he ought to die!

PILATE.　Silence! Am I to crucify your king?

VOICES (*chanting in unison*).　We have no king but Caesar! We have no king but Caesar! We have no king but Caesar!

PILATE (*with authority*).　Silence! (*Placatingly*) Now, remember that on the occasion of this your festival I can release any prisoner whom you choose. Now I have two prisoners here at this very moment—Barabbas, in prison for rioting and murder; and I have this man Jesus who is, as far as I can see, innocent of any crime. Shall I release Jesus to you?

VOICES. No! No! We want Barabbas! (*Taken up as a chant*) We want Barabbas!

PILATE (*with icy authority*). And what am I to do with Jesus, the king of the Jews?

VOICES (*savagely*). Crucify him! Crucify him!

PILATE (*almost desperately*). But why? What crime has he committed?

VOICES (*mingled*). Crucify! Crucify! We want Barabbas!

PILATE (*shouting*). Silence! (*The crowd noises die away to complete silence.*) You shall have what you want. (*He calls*) Centurion, give orders for Barabbas to be released. And as for Jesus the king of the Jews, have him stripped and flogged. He is to be crucified.

(*The crowd gives a bloodthirsty cheer.*)

⁓ 21 ⁓

THE DEATH OF JESUS AND THE
PROMISE OF THE RESURRECTION

And when they were come to the place, which is called
Calvary, there they crucified Jesus, and the malefactors,
one on the right hand, and the other on the left.

*(Murmur of crowd noises against which the following
conversation takes place.)*

OLD SOLDIER. What's the matter, Sergius, my lad? You're
  looking a bit green!
SERGIUS. I'm all right. It's just that it's my first . . .
OLD SOLDIER. Your first crucifixion, eh? Well, don't worry,
  I've seen hundreds, and after a bit you stop thinking
  about them. But I don't feel too happy about this
  fellow in the middle.
SERGIUS (*eagerly*). Neither do I. I've never seen a face
  like his. I believe . . .
OLD SOLDIER (*roughly*). Oh, never mind what you believe.
  I tell you it's no good having pity, or sympathy. If
  you're a soldier of Rome you get your orders, and if
  you know what's good for you, you carry them out.
SERGIUS. But suppose he's innocent?

OLD SOLDIER (*impatiently*). Well, suppose he is! They'll all be dead in a few hours, anyway, so why worry? If you can't bear the sight don't look up. Look down here. Here's their clothes. We're allowed to share them by law, you know. Not much here, I should say—two highway robbers and a field preacher. Oh-ho, what's this? Now here's a beautiful garment, beautiful! Look, every stitch put in by a loving hand, and there's not a seam anywhere!

SERGIUS (*wistfully*). It's a lovely garment. D'you suppose I . . .

OLD SOLDIER (*sharply*). Oh, no, my lad, fair's fair! Share and share alike in the army. Call the others over, and we'll draw lots for it. This is a real prize. (*He calls.*) Come on, lads!

VOICES.
{ All right, soldier.
{ Where's the dice?
{ Come on, sit down.
{ Man, I've got it!

(*Mingled voices, against which* JESUS *speaks.*)

JESUS. Father, forgive them for they know not what they do.

1ST BYSTANDER. Listen, I think he's trying to say something.

2ND BYSTANDER. There's not much he can say now! There's plenty he used to say, claiming to be the Son of God, and all that nonsense.

1ST BYSTANDER. Yes, Jesus, can you hear me? If you're really the Son of God, why don't you step down from your cross and show us. We'd all believe then!

2ND BYSTANDER (*sneeringly*). Why, even the priests would believe you if you did that!

PRIEST. Indeed. This is the final proof to us that his claims were false. If he were really God's Son, God would undoubtedly deliver him.

(Thief groans.)

2ND BYSTANDER. That thief on the cross. What's he trying to say?

THIEF ON CROSS (*abusively*). Yes, why don't you save yourself and us? We're all in the same boat. Call yourself the Son of God—

2ND THIEF ON CROSS. Oh, leave him alone! Can't you tell right from wrong even now? We're only getting what we've deserved. But can't you see this man never did any wrong in his life? Lord, remember me when you come into your kingdom!

JESUS. I tell you truly this very day . . . you will be with me . . . in Paradise.

And it was about the sixth hour, and there was a darkness over all the earth until the ninth hour.

(Scene: Now some yards away from the actual crucifixion, on the outskirts of the crowd.)

(The crowd noises are very much reduced. The SCRIBE *and* NICODEMUS *both speak quietly.)*

SCRIBE. Can you still see him, Nicodemus?

NICODEMUS. Hardly at all, at this distance. This sudden darkness in the middle of the day has certainly scared that bloodthirsty crowd. It's growing strangely still. Even the birds have stopped singing.

SCRIBE. I'm not surprised. This is the blackest day I have ever seen.

NICODEMUS (*reminiscently*). The darkness reminds me that months ago I visited this man, by night—I was fearful of my own reputation. I've always remembered some words of his. He said, "I, if I be lifted up, will draw all men unto me." I wonder if he knew then how it would end?

SCRIBE. Well, he's been lifted up all right. Trust the Romans to think out the foulest way to put a man to death. What with the agony and the cramp, the heat and the flies—oh, dear God, I can't bear to think of it!

NICODEMUS. "If I be lifted up."—Yes I am certain he knew what he was saying.

SCRIBE. He was a good man. But doesn't all this prove he was tragically mistaken? If he had really been the Son of God, none of this could ever have happened.

NICODEMUS. Are you so sure? Perhaps all this is permitted to happen because he *is* the Son of God.

SCRIBE. Do you mean he'll survive this? No! No human being could stand that torture and live!

NICODEMUS. No, I believe he will die. I believe it was in his mind to suffer this unspeakable horror. But I do *not* believe that this is the end.

SCRIBE. You mean—you mean he'll come back to life? But that's impossible!

NICODEMUS. Is it? We shall see.

(*Scene: Now back at the Cross.*)

CENTURION. Stand up, men. Stand by the crosses. I can still see you, black as it is! What's the matter with you, Sergius? You're trembling all over.

SERGIUS. It's this darkness, sir—it's uncanny. Seems like the gods are angry with us.

CENTURION.   That's enough from you, Sergius. Our job is
to see that the execution is carried out—never mind
our feelings. Anyway, the darkness is lifting now, I
think.

JESUS.   Eli, eli, lama sabachthani.

1ST BYSTANDER.   What's that mean? Sounds as if he's
calling for Elijah!

2ND BYSTANDER (*in sudden pity*).   Oh, be quiet, you! I
reckon he's thirsty. (*To the* CENTURION) Centurion, is
it all right for me to push up this spongeful of wine?
I can just about reach his lips with it on my stick.

CENTURION.   All right. But he's pretty nearly gone.

A SCRIBE.   Don't any of you understand your native
tongue? He wasn't calling for a drink. He wasn't calling for Elijah. He called, "My God! My God! why
hast thou forsaken me?"

JESUS (*in exhausted triumph*).   It is finished!

SERGIUS.   Does that mean he's dead, sir?

CENTURION.   No, he's not dead, though he's not long to go
now. But (*in admiration*) didn't any of you hear the
way he said those words? I've seen hundreds of men
crucified, and sooner or later they all crack up. But not
this man. He spoke as though he'd won a victory.
Listen, all of you! He's trying to speak again.

JESUS.   Father, into thy hands I commend my spirit.

SERGIUS.   I reckon he's gone now, sir.

(*There is a heavy reverberating rumble.*)

CENTURION.   Steady, men, steady! Haven't you ever heard
of an earthquake? Our job is to stand by until we get
further orders, so get a grip on yourselves. (*Pause.*)
But (*defiantly*) I tell you that, whatever his own
people say, this Jesus *was* a son of God.

ᴏᴠ 22 ᴏᴠ

THE RESURRECTION OF JESUS

On the first day of the week Mary Magdalene came early,
when it was still dark, to the tomb where they had laid
Jesus, and saw that the stone had been taken away from the
tomb. Then she ran and came to Simon Peter and to the
other disciple whom Jesus loved.

(Knocking.)

PETER.   Who's there?
MARY.   It's me, Mary of Magdala. Open the door, Peter.
PETER.   I'm coming. There . . .

(Door opens.)

JOHN.   Why, what's the matter?
MARY *(breathless, with a hint of tears)*.   Oh, Peter, oh,
     John! It's gone, I tell you it's gone!
PETER.   Here, steady, Mary! *What* has gone? You fright-
     ened us knocking on the door like that!
JOHN.   Come, Mary, sit down and rest for a moment, and
     get your breath back.
MARY.   Oh, thank you, but it's been such a terrible shock.
     What have they *done* with him?

PETER.   What are you talking about, Mary?

JOHN.   Gently, Peter! Can't you see she's upset. Now, Mary, tell us as clearly as you can what you've seen.

MARY.   Well, you see, I got up very early this morning . . . somehow I felt I must visit the Master's grave. I know it was foolish.

JOHN.   Oh, Mary.

MARY.   But I couldn't sleep last night for thinking that we hadn't done all we could for his poor body. You know it all had to be done in such a hurry.

PETER.   But what about the stone, Mary? How ever did you think you were going to move that? You know it took four Roman soldiers to roll it into place. . . .

MARY.   I know, I know. All the way there in the darkness I kept saying to myself, "This is silly, this is silly. Even if the soldiers let you get to the grave, you'll never be be able to move the stone. They'll just laugh at you." And yet, Peter and John, I know you won't understand me, but I *just had to go.*

PETER.   But where's the sense in that? You might have got arrested.

MARY.   But I wasn't, you see! When I got there, there were no guards, no stone, and (*with a sob*) no body of the Master either.

PETER.   What do you mean? The guards had deserted their post?

MARY.   There was no one there at all.

JOHN.   And that huge stone . . . do you mean to tell us that that had disappeared too?

MARY.   No, not disappeared. But it looked as though some great force had flung it back. The tomb's open and empty. His body's gone. Oh, what have they done with him? What have they done with him?

PETER. John, we must go at once and see what has happened.

(Noise of door opening as PETER *sets off.)*

JOHN. Of course. Mary, you stay here where you can rest and be safe.

PETER *(from distance—impatiently)*. Come on, John, there's no time to be lost.

JOHN *(calling)*. Coming, Peter! Good-by, Mary.

(Running footsteps.)

MARY. Good-by. And presently, when it grows light, I will go there again myself.

(Scene: The Tomb in the Garden.)

(Noise of birds as the sun is rising.)

PETER. You go on, John. *(Gasping)* Haven't run like this since I was a child.

JOHN *(calling from distance ahead)*. All right!

PETER. Must get there . . . must see for myself. . . . Women get funny ideas into their heads sometimes, and it was still dark. . . . Any minute now . . . be able to see for myself. Oh! *(in sudden awe)* Dear Father in Heaven, *she was right!* Oh, John, she *was* right. The stone's been moved.

JOHN. Yes, there is no one here at all. I looked inside the tomb. I could see the linen clothes they wrapped his body in. But there's no body there. Peter, I'm scared. What's happened?

PETER. Well, I'm going in. What's there to be afraid of?

(His voice, and subsequent voices inside the tomb have an "echoing" quality.)

John, John, come in and see for yourself!

JOHN.   All right, I'm coming. Peter, look!

PETER.   D'you see, John, all the clothes and the spices that they wrapped the Master's body in . . . not disturbed in the least? But there's no body there!

JOHN.   No, and look! Even the cloth they used to wrap round his head is lying just as it did. Nobody's moved any of these, nobody's undone them. It's just that he's not here.

PETER.   I don't know what to make of it. Let's get outside, John.

JOHN.   All right, Peter.

PETER.   The Master's gone. How, or where, I don't know.

JOHN.   Peter, let's go home and think and pray, and then perhaps we'll understand.

PETER.   Yes, perhaps we'll understand.

Then the disciples went away again unto their own home. But Mary stood outside the tomb, weeping.

MARY (*sobbing*).   Oh, oh, where have they taken him? Someone must know, or was I mistaken? Could his body still be there?—I must look inside the tomb again.

(*Inside the tomb.*)

No, no, only his clothes, only his clothes. Oh, who are these shining figures? Why are they here? Oh, sirs, I'm weeping because they have taken away my Lord, and I do not know where they have laid his body. He is not here . . . not here in this empty tomb . . . not in these empty graveclothes. . . . I must go back to the garden. Perhaps the gardener will know where they have taken him. (*Pause, then outside the tomb*) Oh, sir, you startled me! But *you* must know all that

happens in this garden. Tell me, please tell me, what
have they done with the body of Jesus?

JESUS. Mary!

MARY. Master! Oh, Master!

JESUS. Yes, Mary, it is I, Jesus, your Master. No, do not
hold me now. Go and tell my brothers that I am
risen from the dead. Tell them that I am going to my
Father, and your Father, to my God and to your God.
But do not be afraid, in a little while you shall all see
me in Galilee!

❧ 23 ❧

JESUS APPEARS TO HIS DISCIPLES

Then the same day at evening, being the first day of the week, the doors were shut where the disciples were assembled for fear of the Jews.

ANDREW.   I don't like this, James, I don't like this at all. Here we are shut up in this room with the door locked, just because we're scared to show our noses outside the place. If the Master were here we'd never be huddled together like this.

JAMES.   Oh, Andrew, we've been over this a hundred times, but what can we do? Now that they've killed the Master all our lives are in danger. It's all very well to say, "If only the Master were here." But he's dead, and apparently even his body's been taken away.

ANDREW.   Yes, I don't know what to make of that story Mary of Magdala told us this morning—all that tale about angels and the message that the Master had risen.

JAMES.   She was so excited I could hardly make out what she was saying.

ANDREW.   But she seemed happy enough, I must say.

JAMES.   I know. The fact that the tomb is empty doesn't

seem to me to prove much though. My brother John and Peter went off to see for themselves . . . at least so I hear. But that's hours ago, and it's getting dark now. Let's hope to goodness they haven't been arrested by the soldiers.

(*Loud knocking at the door.*)

ANDREW. Who's that? The Roman guard!

(*More knocking.*)

JOHN (*from outside*). Open the door quickly, James— (*knock*)—it's only your brother John, and Peter's with me.

PETER. Come on, let us in. Quick, we've got the most wonderful news!

(*Noise of unbolting and creak of door.*)

JAMES. Well, what is it?

PETER. *What is it?* The Master's alive! We've seen him . . . he's spoken to us!

ANDREW. Then Mary's story was true?

(*Door is shut.*)

JOHN. Yes, we saw the empty tomb and the graveclothes, soon after she did, but that didn't mean much to us. (*With great confidence*) But since then we've seen him.

PETER. The Master himself!

JOHN. He's spoken to us!

(*Further knocking at door.*)

CLEOPAS (*speaking from outside*). Let us in, please . . . it's Cleopas and a friend. We've got the most wonderful news!

JOHN.   Cleopas! I thought he'd gone back to Emmaus.

(*Noise of door opening.*)

PETER.   Cleopas, come in, come in and welcome! We've
seen the Lord!

JOHN.   He's risen! I tell you he's alive!

CLEOPAS.   Praise God, we've seen him, too!

PETER.   You? When? Where? Tell us quickly, Cleopas!

CLEOPAS.   Well, my friend here and I were walking to
Emmaus, talking about what we thought was this
terrible tragedy. You see we just couldn't understand
how God's Christ should meet such a dreadful end.
And then a stranger walked along with us and asked
us why we were so miserable.

COMPANION.   Yes, we hadn't the slightest idea who he
was. We thought he must be some visitor up from the
country.

CLEOPAS.   We told him he must be the only person in Jerusalem who hadn't heard about it all. "About what?"
he asked. So we told him all that we had believed
about Jesus of Nazareth.

COMPANION.   And then, very kindly and very gently, he
began to tell us that we were being rather stupid and
slow in understanding what the Scripture had said,
about how Christ *must* suffer.

CLEOPAS.   Yes, he began with Moses; then he spoke of the
psalmists and the prophets. He showed us how they all
foretold the sufferings of Christ. Everything became
absolutely clear and our hearts were bursting with
joy, as we realized that the death of Jesus was part of
God's great plan.

COMPANION.   Yes, and by that time we'd got to Emmaus,
and it was beginning to get dark. So, of course we

asked the stranger in to share a meal with us, though he looked as though he wanted to go on farther.

CLEOPAS. But we persuaded him. He came in with us, and we asked him to bless the meal.

COMPANION. That's when it happened! The moment he broke the bread and spoke to the Father, as he always did, we knew who he was. It was Jesus . . . alive! Jesus, who had been talking to us as we walked along.

CLEOPAS. And quite suddenly he vanished, and we rushed back here as fast as we could to tell you that the Lord is risen.

ANDREW. It seems too wonderful to be true.

PETER. But it is true! Many of us have seen him now!

JESUS. (*Appearing suddenly*) Peace be to you, my children!

VOICES. {
It's a spirit!
Don't touch it!
Master!
It's the Lord!
I saw him crucified, he can't be alive!
}

JESUS. My children, why are you so frightened and so slow to believe? It is I myself, the one whom you know and love. Look at my hands and feet. I was indeed crucified, but now I am alive again. Touch me. A spirit has no flesh and bones, and you can see that I have.

VOICES. {
Master!
Can it be true?
Can we believe our eyes?
}

JESUS. So you still find it hard to believe? Did any of you ever hear of a spirit eating food? Give me something to eat and I will show you I am the Jesus whom you have known all this time.

PETER. What have we got in the cupboard, John?

JOHN. Well, there's some fish left over. Oh, and there's a piece of a honeycomb left on this dish.

JESUS. Bring them to me. (*Short pause.*) Now I can see that you're all beginning to believe. But have you not been slow and foolish? Did I not tell you time and again while I was with you before that the Son of Man must suffer and must die, and on the third day rise from the dead?

VOICES. {
It is the Master.

Lord, forgive me, I know it's you now.

Master, we had forgotten. Of course, you said you would rise again!

Oh, praise God . . . it's true! He's alive!
}

JESUS. Yes, I am alive forever. But now sit down, all of you. My disciples, all that has happened was foretold in the Scriptures, and the plan of the Father has been fulfilled in the Son of Man. For the whole world must know what God has done, and you are to be my witnesses.

❧ 24 ❧

JESUS APPEARS IN GALILEE

After these things Jesus showed himself again to the
disciples at the sea of Galilee; and in this way he showed
himself.

*(Noise of lapping water and occasional cry of wild
fowl, creaking cord or flap of idle sail.)*

NATHANAEL. B-r-r-r . . . it's cold out here on the lake
just before sunrise! How can you stand there, Peter,
without a stitch on?

PETER. I never did feel the cold much, Nathanael, and
this morning I don't feel it at all. Now that we know
that the Lord is alive I feel so full of joy that nothing
can touch me! The only thing is, I'm terribly hungry.

NATHANAEL. Well, so are we all, James and John and the
rest of us! *(In mock anger)* I can't think why we ever
came out with you. I thought you fishermen knew your
business and we've spent the whole night here and
caught nothing at all. What do you say to that, John
and you, James, . . . you were fishermen?

JAMES. We still are . . . but there's no accounting for
luck.

JOHN.   It's all part of the game. Sometimes you can spend the whole night waiting for a catch. At other times you run into a shoal and you're afraid your nets are going to break.

PETER.   Do you remember that time the Master told us just where to cast the net? And we very nearly did tear it that time. I've never seen such a catch in all my life.

NATHANAEL.   Quiet a minute, Peter. I think there's someone calling from the shore . . . It seems to be coming from over there.

JESUS (*from the shore*).   Ahoy there!

PETER.   Can't see who it is in this mist . . . what's he saying?

JESUS.   Have you caught anything to eat?

PETER.   No . . . not a thing!

JESUS.   Cast your net on the starboard side of the boat—there's a good haul there!

PETER.   Right! Might as well do as he says. Come on, lads, heave her overboard once more. There she goes.

(*Splash as net is thrown overboard.*)

JAMES.   And there are the fish, straight away, just like that!

NATHANAEL.   And big ones too—a marvelous catch!

PETER.   Hold that net, James, steady, John!

JOHN (*in an urgent whisper*).   Peter, Peter, do you know who that is on the shore? It's the Lord!

PETER.   The Lord, and me as naked as the day I was born! Here, throw me something to put on! I'm going to swim ashore—the rest of you can bring in the catch!

(*Peter dives in.*)

JOHN.   Well, that's a fine thing, leaving us to do all the work.

JAMES (*calling*). Come on, lads. Haul the net in close. (*Groans*) We'll have to tow it ashore. It's only about a hundred yards, and John's sure the Lord is waiting for us!

NATHANAEL. The Lord! Come on, lads, get the oars out.

VOICES. { The Lord!
{ The Lord!

(*Noise of oars and rowlocks.*)

NATHANAEL. Quick as you can, there!

JAMES (*quietly to John*). John, can't you guess why Peter was in such a hurry? It's that business of . . . well, that denial . . .

JOHN. Of course, I'd forgotten all about it. (*Calling*) Come on now, all of you, pull for the shore. We're nearly there.

(*Splashing of oars and grunting.*)

JAMES. Why, there's a fire burning!

NATHANAEL (*joyfully*). I believe I can smell food.

JOHN. And the Master's waiting for us on the shore.

(*Boat crunching on beach—lapping water and men disembarking.*)

JESUS. Come on, lads, your breakfast's all ready and waiting. And Peter, you'd better fetch some of the fish you've just caught.

PETER. Right, Master!

NATHANAEL. We're hungry all right!

VOICES. { This is wonderful!
{ Worth staying up all night for, eh?

(*Fade into murmur of voices, and fade out.*)

So when they had finished the meal Jesus spoke to Simon Peter.

JESUS.   Simon, son of John, do you love me more than the others?

PETER.   Yes, Lord you know that I am . . . your friend.

JESUS.   Then feed my lambs. Simon, son of John, do you love me?

PETER.   Yes, Lord, you know that I am your friend.

JESUS.   Then look after my sheep. (*Pause.*) Simon, son of John, *are* you my friend?

PETER.   Lord, you know everything . . . everything about me. You must see that I am your friend!

JESUS.   Then feed my sheep. Simon, when you were young, you took charge of your own life and went where you chose, but when you are old someone else will take charge of you and will lead you to a place you did not choose. (*Briskly*) But *now,* you are to follow me!

PETER.   Lord, I will try to follow you always. But what about the others, what about John, who's coming toward us now? What is *his* future going to be?

JESUS.   Simon, that is no business of yours. Your concern is to follow me, now and always. And so it must be for each one of my disciples today and every day. You are to follow me!

∾ 25 ∾

THE ASCENSION

(*Murmur of conversation.*)

PETER. This is the day and this is the place. How like the Lord to have chosen this hillside for us to meet him for the last time! Are we all here?

JOHN. Yes, Peter, all Eleven of us, and I imagine every one of us is wondering what the Lord is going to say to us today.

JAMES. Ah, what stories we could tell between us of the last few weeks; what do you say, Andrew?

ANDREW. Yes, James, every one of us is convinced now that our Master who was crucified is alive and Lord of all.

JOHN. Think, only a few weeks ago we were the most discouraged and fearful men you could find anywhere! And now I believe we're the most determined.

JAMES. With the power the Lord has promised us we're all of us going to do great things for him, eh, Thomas?

THOMAS. He's my Lord and my God. That I know for certain, until I die . . . and beyond. It doesn't much matter to me now whether I see him, or whether I don't. I know he's with us always.

PETER. Of course. I think that's been the reason why, during these last few weeks, he's sometimes allowed us to see him, and sometimes he hasn't. Just to let us get used to the idea that he's always with us, even when we don't see him. What do you all think?

JAMES. I'm sure that's partly true, Peter.

JOHN. But it's not all the truth. For instance, since he rose from the dead he's taught us things which we simply wouldn't have understood before.

ANDREW. And then there's this promise he has often made of sending us power. . . . Someone to stand by us and strengthen us.

PETER. Yes, we shall need that. Nobody knows better than I do that it's easy enough to make a bold speech, but we need strength and power inside us . . . the same sort of spirit that he had, he *has* I mean.

THOMAS. We shall need his presence if we're going to build his Kingdom.

JAMES. Especially if it's the Lord's will to restore the Kingdom to Israel.

JESUS. Peace be with you, my children!

PETER. Master!

JAMES. Lord, we are all here waiting for you.

ANDREW. Master, we know you're with us always, but it's good to see you.

THOMAS. Lord, we all believe in you with all our hearts.

JOHN. And we will do whatever you say.

PETER. Yes, Lord, we are ready. But, tell us . . . is it here in Israel that your Kingdom will come? Is the power to be given again to our nation—to the Father's chosen people?

JESUS. It is not for any of you to know the times of the Father's plan; they belong to him alone. But all of you, who have been with me so long, will receive the power of the Holy Spirit. You must not leave Jerusalem until you have been given this power from God. But when you have received it; you will be witnesses of the truth that I have taught you. You will be witnesses not only in Jerusalem, not only in Judaea, not only in Samaria but to the far corners of the earth. You are to take the Good News to every nation upon earth; you are to give them my teaching, baptizing them in the name of the Father, and of the Son and of the Holy Spirit. Remember all power belongs to me, and I am with you always to the end of the world.

PETER (*very meekly*).   Master, O Master!

JOHN.   Lord, we will do exactly as you say.

THOMAS.   My Lord and my God!

JESUS.   Now the time has come for me to return to the Father. Peace I leave with you, my peace I give to you.

(*Music.*)

And while they looked steadfastly toward heaven, behold, two men stood by them in white robes; who said to them, Men of Galilee, why do you stand gazing up into heaven? This same Jesus, who is taken up from you into heaven, shall so come in like manner as you have seen him go into heaven.

PETER.   Praise be to Christ, the Son of the living God! We must do as the Lord said.

ANDREW.   And go back to Jerusalem.

JAMES.   He will be with us always.

JOHN.   We'll wait until the promise comes.

ANDREW.   Amen to that.

THOMAS.   We must do what he told us.
PETER.   We are his witnesses.
ANDREW.   To preach the good news.
JOHN.   To the end of the world.

(*Murmurs of assent with these remarks emerging.*)

JAMES.   Praise to the God of our fathers, and to his Christ!
THOMAS.   Thank God for this day, and for all that we have
    seen and heard.
ANDREW.   Thanks be to God.
PETER.   Praise be to Christ, the Son of the living God!
JOHN.   Praise be to him indeed!

And they worshiped him and turned back to Jerusalem
with great joy. And when they were come into the city
they went into an upper room. And they all continued with
one accord in prayer and supplication.

ᐁ 26 ᐁ

THE GIFT OF THE HOLY SPIRIT

Now, when the day of Pentecost had come the disciples were all together in one place.

JOHN (*eagerly and with some awe*). Peter, do you think the Lord will send his gift today?

PETER. I know no more about when the Spirit will come, John, than any of us.

JOHN. It would be like the Lord to choose the height of the festival.

JAMES. I feel the moment is near now.

ANDREW. And so do I.

JAMES. Well, we've waited . . .

JOHN. And we've prayed.

THOMAS. We know we can trust him.

MATTHEW. Yes, the gift will come.

THOMAS. It will be like having him here again!

ANDREW. He promised to be *in* us as well as *with* us.

MATTHEW. That means we shall be full of his joy!

PETER. Yes, and his courage too!

JAMES. We shall be able to speak with authority!

MATTHEW. Just as he did.

JOHN. Perhaps we shall be able to heal!

ANDREW.   No one will be able to stop us!

MATTHEW.   We shall go out in his name.

ANDREW.   Yes, and with his power within us.

PETER (*praying fervently*).   Lord, we believe. (*Apostles repeat.*) Lord, we are ready. (*Apostles repeat.*) Lord, we await your gift, Lord, send down your Spirit upon us as you promised.

(*Sound of a rushing mighty wind: apostles' voices full of excited joy and may "overlap."*)

MATTHEW.   Lord, Lord, this joy.

THOMAS.   This power, this fire!

ANDREW.   Praise God, we know what we must do!

PETER.   Dear Lord, the strength has come.

JOHN.   O Lord and God, this joy is too much to bear. . . .

JAMES.   And your love is within us.

MATTHEW.   Yes, every man must know of your great love.

JOHN.   All the barriers are gone.

JAMES.   We must tell the world!

PETER.   Oh, praise God in the Highest!

VOICES.   { Amen.
            { Amen.

And they were all filled with the Holy Spirit, and began to speak in other languages as the Spirit gave them power to speak. And there were dwelling at Jerusalem, Jews, devout men, from every nation under heaven. And when this sound was heard, the multitude came together.

(*A loud murmur of voices.*)

PETER (*almost incoherent with excitement, and yet speaking with authority*).   God, the God of our fathers bids me speak to you! God has come upon us! God has filled our hearts! God is speaking through our very lips. He has done a great and marvelous thing and we must speak. We must tell you what we know! In the name of the Lord Jesus Christ we declare to you all that we have seen. . . .

(*Fade out* PETER'S *voice, and bring in following voices.*)

1ST BYSTANDER.   There's a miracle, if you like!

2ND BYSTANDER.   Miracle? Where?

1ST BYSTANDER.   Well, can't you see that every man jack of this crowd can understand what this fellow Peter, and the others, are saying? And everyone of *them* is a Galilean . . . we know that! Now look at the crowd . . . where's that fellow from, do you think?

2ND BYSTANDER.   Oh, Egypt, at a guess.

1ST BYSTANDER.   And that one?

2ND BYSTANDER.   Persia, without a doubt!

1ST BYSTANDER.   And that dark-skinned fellow, over there?

2ND BYSTANDER.   Er, North Africa . . . Libya, I should imagine.

1ST BYSTANDER.   And that Greek-looking youth?

2ND BYSTANDER.   Oh, Crete, possibly.

1ST BYSTANDER.   Well, *now* do you see what I mean? There are at least a dozen different nationalities, and at least a dozen different languages.

2ND BYSTANDER (*musingly*).   Of course I know a little Arabic and some Persian and a bit of Greek myself.

1ST BYSTANDER (*excitedly*).   Yet everybody here can plainly understand what's being said! What's going on? A trick or a miracle?

(*Disturbed murmurs of the crowd with one or two remarks emerging from them.*)

VOICES.
{
What's that you say?
Are we being tricked or something?
Explain! Explain!
Why, that fellow who's speaking is a Galilean!
How can we all hear in our own native language?
I'll tell you what it is—they're drunk!
}

(*Crowd laughs and chatters.*)

PETER (*very excitedly, but speaking with authority*). Listen to me, all of you! We are not drunk, at least not drunk with wine! We are filled with the Spirit of the living God. Don't you remember the promise God gave through his prophet? He said, "I will pour out my Spirit on my servants and they shall speak with power." This is what is happening now. The promise of God has come true. God has poured out his Spirit.

VOICE. What did I tell you? Drunk, that's what they are, drunk.

ANOTHER VOICE. Quiet—quiet there! Listen to the man, can't you?

(*Cries of "Hush! Hush!" Then crowd becomes silent as* PETER *resumes.*)

PETER. Yes, we are drunk, if you like, but drunk with the Spirit of God! We are full of the joy of God, full of the certainty of God, and every man among you, wherever you come from, must listen to what God commands us to say.

Only a few weeks ago there lived among us a man. He was Jesus of Nazareth. Many of you knew him. You heard him speak, saw him heal. You saw in him the unmistakable signs of God's power. This man, who was full of all goodness and free from all sin, was condemned by the leaders of Israel and crucified under the law of Rome. Yet all of these men standing here with me are eyewitnesses to a most extraordinary fact. The Man whom you crucified, God raised from the dead! We have all seen him, we have spoken to him, and we have heard him speak. We have even touched him. We know beyond any doubt that this Man Jesus is alive today, and alive for ever. We know that this Jesus, whom Israel crucified, God has shown to be His Christ, and the Lord of all!

VOICE. My brothers, what shall we do now?

ANOTHER VOICE. Yes, if what you say is true, how can Israel find forgiveness?

PETER. You must repent, every one of you! You must be baptized in the name of this same Lord Jesus Christ. Then you too will have your sins forgiven. You too will receive the gift of the Holy Spirit. For the Day has arrived! The Promise has come true! God is pouring out His Spirit upon all who will accept the Lord Jesus Christ. God calls to every man, whether he be near or far, to believe in Christ, the Son of the living God.

Then they that gladly received his word were baptized; and the same day there were added unto them about three thousand souls. And they continued steadfastly in the apostles' teaching and fellowship, and in breaking of bread, and in prayers. And the Lord added to the church daily such as were being saved.